S0-EDM-229

"Art and nature, the two great phenomena of our environment, are so closely related that one is inconceivable without the other, and it will never be possible to force them into the formula of a definition."

Karl Nierendorf, 1928.

From the infinite universe to the infinitely small and from reality to dreams, time reigns supreme.
It governs nature, an inexhaustible wellspring of inspiration, which generates our emotions and results in the most authentic imaginable forms of art.
From time immemorial, painters, poets and musicians have immersed themselves in nature. Its colours, its light, its sounds and its varied kinds of matter have given rise to the most fascinating works of art. This too is how the master-watchmakers at Jaeger-LeCoultre imagine timekeepers that are original as they are timeless: both form and function reflect the constant renewal of life's vital processes.
As in nature, harmony prevails and nothing is left to chance. Between the present moment and eternity, each element is at once unique and an integral part of a whole. Thus it is that within the Manufacture, eye, hand and heart are guided by absolute truth, the immutable laws of the universe, the authenticity of time created in the image of the cosmos.

Contents

I

In the cradle of time

A destiny in time

The Vallée de Joux

Polar landscape, icy blue sky. The frozen lake of the Vallée de Joux testifies to the harsh winters that make this valley a truly exceptional place.

Since the farm-workshop in 1833, where Antoine LeCoultre developed the first gear-wheels and his patented watch mechanisms, the Manufacture has built several extensions. It has brought together all the professions required to form a watchmaking complex that is unique in its kind.

At 1,000 metres in the Jura hills of Switzerland's canton of Vaud, lies a valley called the Vallée de Joux, a name with magical connotations for those who appreciate and collect fine watchmaking. The valley, with its twin lakes bounded by forested hills, is famous for its harsh and persistent winters. Houses are clad in metal against westerly gales.

In the 16th century, Huguenots sought refuge from religious persecution in this secluded valley and began to develop their craft skills with puritanical tenacity. Specializing in metalwork, they raised their art to the manufacture of the first mechanical devices, such as music boxes, automatons and watch components. By the 19th century, the valley dwellers, known as "Combiers", were acquiring every conceivable manual skill in the art of making watches, developing a degree of proficiency unequalled in the world.

Today, many people recognize the Vallée de Joux as the home of the world's best watchmakers. The LeCoultre family, in particular, made a name for themselves through unrelenting industry and constant invention. And it is in the village of Le Sentier, in 1833, that the chronicle of the Jaeger-LeCoultre watch Manufacture begins. In 1803, Le Sentier saw the birth of a boy who was to make the name

LeCoultre, one half of a magic formula.

Antoine LeCoultre. The founder's influence lives on in the timepieces made by Jaeger-LeCoultre.

Jacques-David LeCoultre. He made a major contribution to giving the Manufacture its international dimension.

Edmond Jaeger. After decades of close ties, he became a partner, adding his name to the Manufacture.

The Vallée de Joux nestles at the heart of the Swiss Jura region, at an altitude of 1,000 metres. Bordered by wooded mountains, it keeps jealous watch over its twin lakes.

LeCoultre world-renowned.
A descendant of Pierre LeCoultre who settled in Le Sentier in 1559, Antoine LeCoultre was the son of Henri-David, owner of a forge that produced mechanical instruments. It was here that he completed his apprenticeship and specialized in metallurgy and gear mechanisms. At the age of 30, Antoine left the family workshops and founded a company manufacturing watch gearing with his brother Ulysse in their native village. He invested his energy and engineering talent in the development of new production processes and methods. The growing enterprise made watch blanks as well as precision parts and was a source of new ideas and innovations. By 1860, it employed 100 people; by 1890, it had produced a range of 125 different movements.
Antoine LeCoultre's sons, Elie, Paul and Benjamin, followed him in the business. LeCoultre became an early source of complicated movements, creating repeaters, chronographs and calendars.
By the time Elie's son, Jacques-David, joined the business in 1899, it had become the Vallée de Joux's leading manufacturer.
It was Jacques-David who, in 1903, entered into a business relationship in Paris with the chronometer-maker Edmond Jaeger. Under its new name of Jaeger-LeCoultre, the Manufacture increased its renown while remaining faithful to Antoine LeCoultre's pioneering spirit.
Staunchly individualist, it has filed hundreds of patents since 1833 and become the enduring reference for the authentically fine Swiss watch.

A journey through the years

Chronicle of authenticity

1851. The first Universal Exhibition opens in London. Antoine LeCoultre wins his first gold medal there.

1844.
Antoine LeCoultre's Millionometer. Invented for measuring in microns.

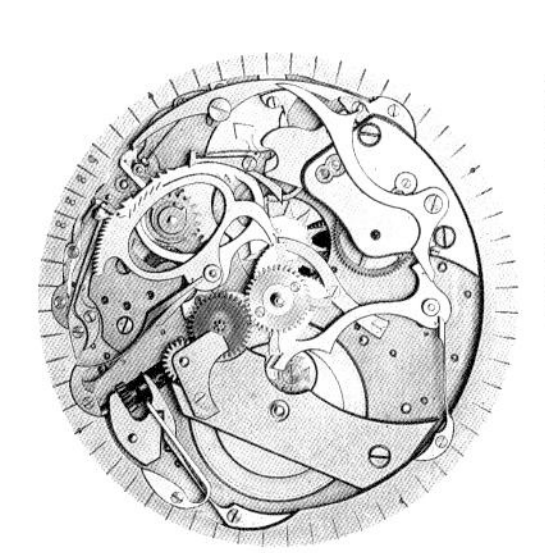

Late 19th century. Movement for an ultra-thin minute-repeater pocket-watch.

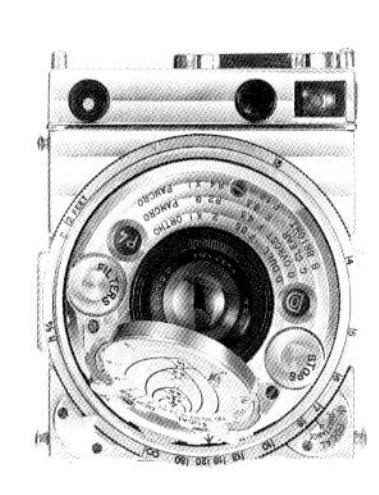

1938.
A favourite with spies, the miniature Compass camera by Jaeger-LeCoultre boasts all the latest technical features.

In the early 18th century, the leading watch manufacturers were the French and the British. Both were sea-faring people with merchant fleets and navies that needed precise time-keeping to navigate the globe. However, by the mid-19th century, their watchmaking dominance was undermined by Swiss watchmakers who began turning out high-value watches in greater quantities. The portable timepiece, once a symbol of rule and power, became available to a wider population.

At the same time, watchmaking came under new influences. One of the sources of fresh ideas and opportunities was Antoine LeCoultre, who designed and built machine-tools that could produce watch-parts to unprecedented levels of precision. Among these was his Millionometer, which established the metric system as the watch-industry measurement standard. In 1847, Antoine LeCoultre developed a crown winding system that also set the time. His successors have inherited his pioneering spirit: since 1833, the Manufacture has filed hundreds of patents. Within a few decades, LeCoultre & Co. had become a leading Swiss watchmaker, delivering an increasingly large number of movements. In 1890, it produced a range of 125 different movements, and, in 1903, its workshops unveiled the slimmest ever movement for pocket-watches. At 1.38 mm thick, it remains an unbroken record. Other exceptionally thin movements followed: a 2.8 mm chronograph and a 2.7 mm minute-repeater.

A former movement-blank workshop in the Manufacture, which, at the beginning of the 19th century, constituted a state-of-the-art production facility in terms of watchmaking technology.

As wristwatches superseded pocket-watches, LeCoultre found new fields to conquer. The tiny wristwatches of the Art Deco era were fitted with the twin-level rectangular Duoplan movement, invented in 1925. It was followed in 1929 by Calibre 101 – still the smallest mechanical watch movement ever made and still in production. In 1928, a revolutionary clock appeared. The Atmos was the only clock that derived its energy from the slightest temperature changes of the surrounding air.

The Reverso, which was introduced in 1931, is among the world's best-known watches and, as an Art Deco classic, has become part of the history of the decorative-arts movement. The 50s and 60s saw a number of innovative wristwatches. The Geomatic housed a chronometer movement; and the Geophysic had special antimagnetic protection as well. The remarkable Calibre 497 automatic movement in the Futurematic watch of 1953 needed no winding crown, and the Memovox of 1956 was the first automatic alarm wristwatch. After the "quartz years" that nearly put an end to mechanical watches, the pent-up ideas in the Manufacture were suddenly released in 1980, resulting in a series of watchmaking achievements that were new to the world. The Manufacture's Book of Timepieces tells the story of their past and their future.

1833. Antoine LeCoultre set up his very first movement-blank workshop in his parents' farmhouse.

1833:
Antoine LeCoultre establishes his watch-making workshop in Le Sentier. It is still a manufacture today, where the watch components are crafted, finished and assembled by hand in a single complex of specialized workshops. This way of making watches calls for infinite time and patience, but without these qualities, watchmakers would be unable to express the love for their craft by finishing and decorating each detail of the watch to perfection.

1844:
Antoine LeCoultre invents his Millionometer, the first instrument capable of measuring components to the nearest micron – a millionth of a metre – and establishes the metric system as the watch industry's measurement standard.

1847:
LeCoultre & Co. produces the first movement with a crown winding system that also sets the time, meaning keys are no longer necessary for winding watches.

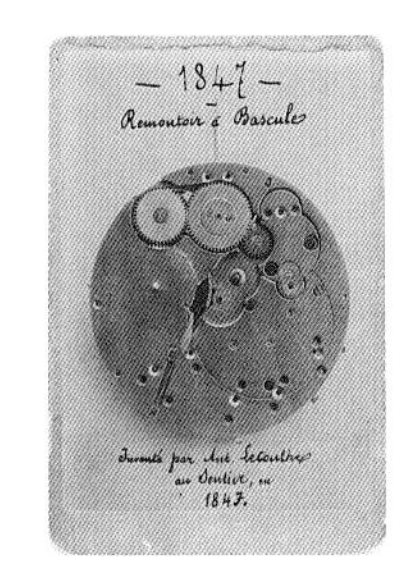

1847. Invention of the crown winding system.

1851:
At the first Universal Exhibition in London, Antoine LeCoultre wins a gold medal for the creation of a gold chronometer with the new keyless winding and setting system.

Late 19th century. Lépine Chronograph – instant 30-minute counter. 19‴ LeCoultre Calibre.

1903:
LeCoultre & Co. unveils the world's flattest pocket-watch calibre. At 1.38 mm thick, it remains an unbroken record. Other exceptionally thin movements follow, such as a 2.8 mm chronograph and a 2.7 mm minute-repeater.

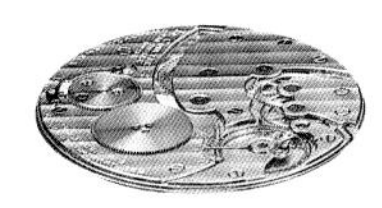

1903. At 1.38 mm, this wafer-thin pocket-watch movement remains unsurpassed.

1925:
A new creative era, and new fields to conquer. Tiny Art Deco watches from LeCoultre & Co., which feature the twin-level rectangular Duoplan movement, are way ahead of their time in terms of their easily interchangeable movement concept and accurate time-keeping.

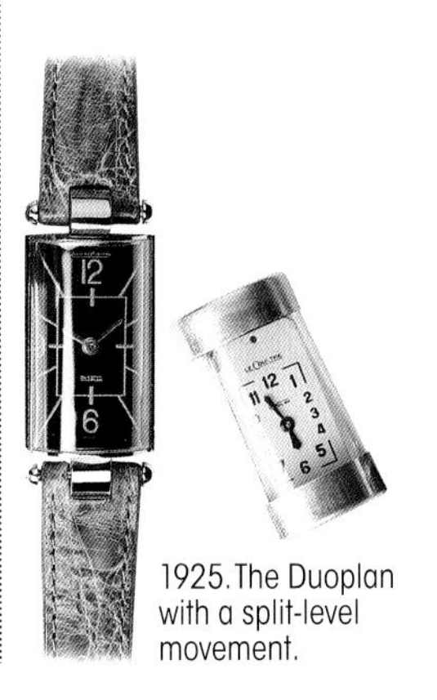

1925. The Duoplan with a split-level movement.

1928. Atmos prototype,
by Jean-Léon Reutter, an engineer from Neuchâtel.

1928:
The engineer J.-L. Reutter invents the remarkable Atmos clock, which never requires winding and derives all the power it needs from tiny changes in air temperature. Since 1936, it is still a favourite government gift, often presented to distinguished visitors to Switzerland.

1929:
LeCoultre & Co. reduces the mechanical watch movement to its smallest dimensions ever. Calibre 101, measuring 14 x 4.8 x 3.4 mm, comprising 98 parts and weighing around 1 gram, is still the world's smallest mechanical movement and is still in production.

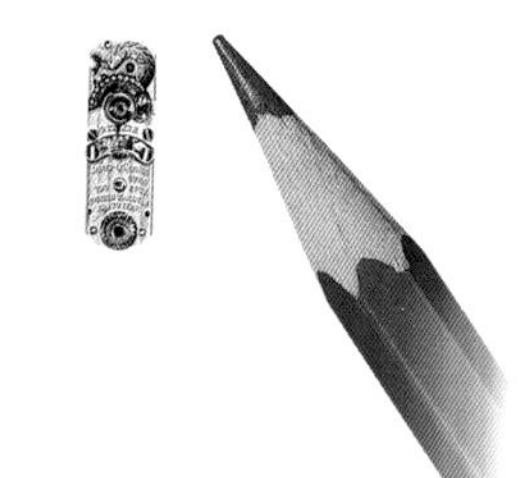

1929. Calibre 101 remains the world's smallest mechanical movement.

1931:
In Le Sentier, the Manufacture LeCoultre & Co. begins to build the Reverso, an artistic reflection of an era in search of purity. This wristwatch with a swivel case turns its back on shocks to protect the fragile glass. It is one of the few remaining authentic Art Deco creations.

The first advertisement, illustrating the unique Reverso swivel.

1932:
The harmonious linear arrangement of the Baguette clock movement is always presented in a glass case.

1953:
Jaeger-LeCoultre develops the Futurematic, equipped with a power-reserve indicator. Fitted with the remarkable Calibre 497, it is the first automatic watch to require no winding crown.

1953. Futurematic. First automatic watch with no winding crown (model from 1956).

1956:
Memovox, the first automatic alarm wristwatch, echoes the effervescence of the 50s. It also blazes the trail for other remarkable inventions such as the Geomatic with its chronometer movement, and the Geophysic chronometer featuring special antimagnetic protection. The ensuing "quartz" years nearly put an end to the mechanical watch. But not in Le Sentier, where the Manufacture continues to follow its own creative

star, while patiently studying ways to scale new heights, using the new technologies. In 1980, its pent-up ideas are finally released, resulting in a series of watchmaking achievements that amaze the world.

1956. Memovox. First automatic wristwatch alarm.

1982:
Jaeger-LeCoultre wins the contest for the smallest quartz movement. Calibre 601 measures 9.7 x 11.7 mm and is just 1.8 mm thick. It proves a decisive victory for the Manufacture in its determination to pursue miniaturization and achieve ever greater precision.

1982. Calibre 601. Tiny quartz movement.

1987:
The smallest chronograph movement emerges from the Manufacture. The Calibre 630 mecha-quartz movement combines the complexity of a mechanical chronograph with quartz precision.

1987. The Odysseus watch is equipped with the first mecha-quartz chronograph movement.

1989:
A new creation by Jaeger-LeCoultre arouses the interest of the entire world: the Grand Réveil. It is an automatic perpetual calendar wristwatch with moon phases and a unique feature – a bronze alarm-bell struck by a hammer.

1989. Grand Réveil. Perpetual calendar and striking mechanism on bronze bell.

1991:
Jaeger-LeCoultre celebrates the 60th birthday of the Reverso, the world's longest-running watch model, with a special limited edition of 500 of this legendary swivel watch, a travelling exhibition entitled "Journey to the centre of time" and a lavishly illustrated book "Reverso. The living legend".

In 1991, the Reverso 60ème opens the era of complicated Reversos.

1992:
In Le Sentier, the most thoroughly-tested timepiece of its era is put through its paces. The Master Control

1000 Hours sets a new standard for mechanical reliability.

1992. The Master Control 1000 Hours watch sets new standards in the reliability of automatic wristwatches.

1993:
The Reverso Tourbillon with power-reserve indicator emerges in a limited edition of 500.

1994:
The small, clear sound of tiny hammers striking acoustic-steel gongs is heard from the first of 500 Reverso Répétition Minutes.
The same year, the Reverso Duo unveils its double life driven by a single mechanical movement: two dials back to back, with their hands turning in the opposite direction, display the time here and now... and at the far ends of the earth.

1994. The Reverso Duo affords the rare pleasure of owning two watches in one.

1996:
The Master Geographic is voted Watch of the Year by the Swiss public. Meanwhile, collectors of fine watchmaking vie with each other for the Reverso Chronographe Rétrograde, crafted in a limited series of 500.

1996. In creating the Master Geographic with multiple time-zones, Jaeger-LeCoultre's master-watchmakers add a genuine masterpiece to their hall of fame.

1997:
The day on one side and the night on the other: the Reverso Duetto is dedicated to the elegance of time in all circumstances. At the heart of its dual nature, it houses the smallest mechanical movement indicating time on the front and back.

1997. The Reverso Duetto expresses brilliant duality within a single time-keeper: front by day, back by night.

1998:
A precious invitation to travel, the Reverso Géographique is born. In addition to multiple time-zones, it is enriched by the display of the perpetual course of the sun and stars. This fifth Limited series of 500 wins first prize for innovation in Germany and Italy. In the meantime, Jaeger-LeCoultre achieves a new feat: the Reverso Gran'Sport in automatic and manually-wound Chronographe Rétrograde versions

combines watchmaking technology with the art of living the present to the full.

1998. The Reverso Gran'Sport heralds a new era in sports watches.

1999:
In tribute to the new millennium, the Manufacture creates an entirely original version of its great Atmos classic. With its quasi-perpetual movement, the Atmos du Millénaire displays the years, months and moon phases over a 1000-year period. This same creative firmament witnesses the emergence of a beautiful star performer: the Reverso Sun Moon. It brings several complications within the orbit of its Grande Taille case: moon phases, day/night indication and power-reserve.

1999. The Atmos du Millénaire guides you through the third millennium, calmly leading you towards the fourth.

2000:
The inimitable encapsulation of rare and specific talents, the Master Grande Memovox adds a unique combination to the Master Control range: perpetual calendar and alarm. And to conclude the succession of Limited series of 500, the Manufacture creates the most complicated rectangular movement ever made for the Reverso: the perpetual calendar.

2000. Reverso Quantième Perpétuel. With the 6th Grande Taille Limited series in pink gold, a collection culminates in eternity.

2001:
The Reverso Platinum Number One celebrates the 70th anniversary of the Reverso and inaugurates a new dynasty of Limited series of 500. A genuine masterpiece, it is the first Reverso movement with an openworked movement. Transparently revealing the art and passion of the Manufacture, its Grande Taille case opens a new chapter in the history of the legendary swivel: that of platinum. The Manufacture Jaeger-LeCoultre has consistently produced numerous landmark innovations that find their way untouched through the ages and its creative vocation is in perpetual motion. The fascinating inventions that will leave their indelible imprint on the future of watchmaking tradition are already leading you towards the fourth millennium.

2001. The Reverso Platinum Number One marks the start of the new Reverso Limited series.

Boasting over 40 different trades and 20 cutting-edge technologies, Jaeger-LeCoultre brings together under one roof a passionately enthusiastic horological workforce. These gifted individuals create watches and clocks which continue to make watchmaking history, as is clearly shown by the long list of patents shown hereafter.

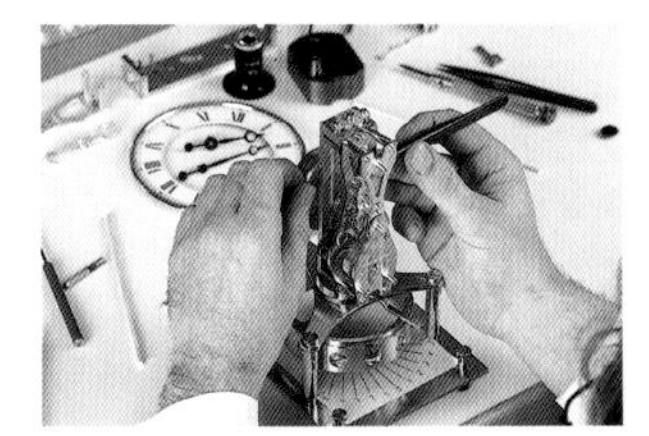

Adjustment

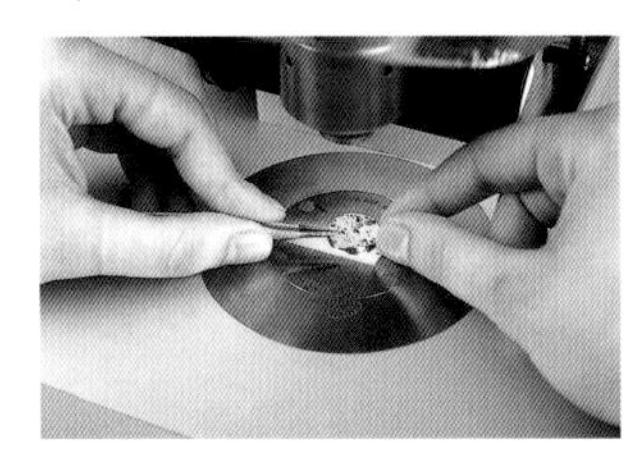

Jewelling

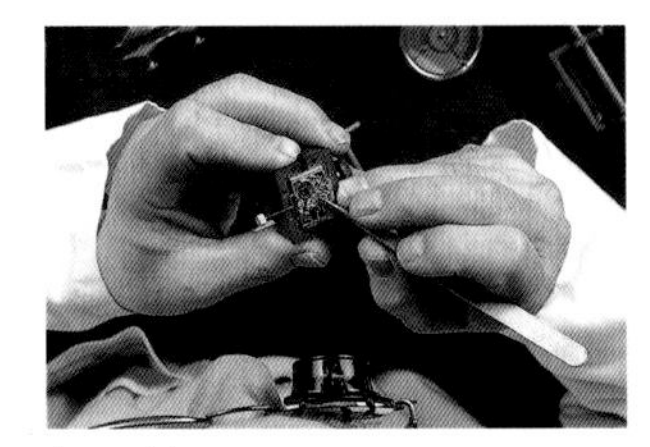

Assembly

Testing

Engraving

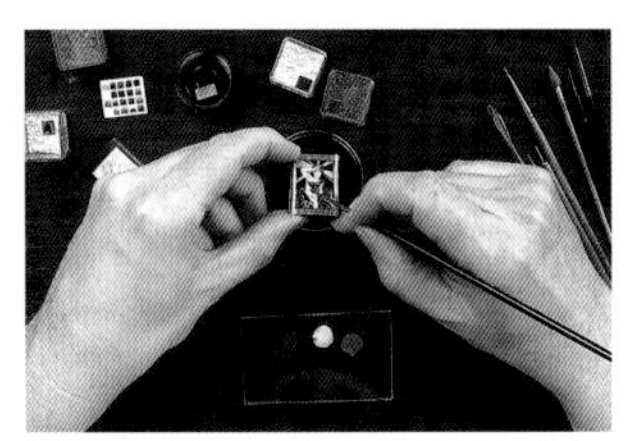

Enamelling

F	176 229 a	22.05.1886	LeCoultre & Cie	Safety pinion.
F	176 778 g	15.06.1886	(Ed. Jaeger)	Spring development.
CH	3218 a	15.01.1891	LeCoultre & Cie	Semi-visible strip click.
CH	3818 bc	21.07.1891	LeCoultre & Cie	Minute counter for chrono repeater.
CH	3847 b	28.07.1891	LeCoultre & Cie	Chrono lever.
CH	3849 b	01.08.1891	LeCoultre & Cie	Instantaneous chrono counters.
CH	4420 b	25.01.1892	LeCoultre & Cie	Instantaneous jumping chrono.
CH	4654 a	22.02.1892	LeCoultre & Cie	Semi-visible pawl click.
CH	4750 h	26.02.1892	LeCoultre & Cie	Index precision adjustment.
CH	5682 b	28.09.1892	LeCoultre & Cie	Instantaneous counter chrono lever.
CH	7905 c	27.01.1894	LeCoultre & Cie	Modulus minute repetition.
CH	9321 a	04.12.1894	LeCoultre & Cie	Semi-visible click, hidden spring.
CH	9397 a	08.12.1894	LeCoultre & Cie	Screwless click.
CH	9406 b	13.12.1894	LeCoultre & Cie	Safety for instantaneous counter.
CH	9409 c	15.12.1894	Benjamin LeCoultre	Repetition: pendant control.
CH	9755 c	18.01.1895	Benjamin LeCoultre	Repetition: pendant control.
CH	9689 c	25.01.1895	Benjamin LeCoultre	Repetition: pendant control.
CH	9690 c	25.01.1895	Benjamin LeCoultre	Repeater mechanism.
CH	9700 c	31.01.1895	LeCoultre & Cie	Repeater: striking mechanism regulator.
CH	9776 c	12.02.1895	Benjamin LeCoultre	Repetition: pendant control.
CH	10 873 a	04.09.1895	LeCoultre & Cie	Capped barrel bridge.
CH	10 874 c	17.09.1895	LeCoultre & Cie	Repetition: silent regulator.
CH	11 661 a	10.02.1896	LeCoultre & Cie	Time-setting.
CH	11 858 c	16.03.1896	LeCoultre & Cie	Repetition: silent regulator.
CH	14 638 a	17.07.1897	LeCoultre & Cie	Recoil click.
CH	27 775 n	31.03.1903	Benjamin LeCoultre	Reservoir level tap.
CH	46 221	01.03.1909	Edmond Jaeger	Pendant-watch.
CH	50 854	19.02.1910	Edmond Jaeger	Schutter watch.
F	427 532	18.03.1911	Edmond Jaeger	Water-resistant case.
CH	101 851	28.09.1921	Et. Ed. Jaeger SA	Power-reserve indicator.
CH	104 138	30.06.1922	Et. Ed. Jaeger SA	Movement for ring-watch.
CH	104 600	30.06.1922	Et. Ed. Jaeger SA	Ring-watch.
CH	111 406 b	20.10.1924	LeCoultre & Cie	Chronoflight operating mechanism.
CH	114 140 a	06.06.1925	LeCoultre & Cie	GH time-setting and winding.
CH	117 392 l	24.12.1925	LeCoultre & Cie	Under-crown for Duoplan.
CH	140 771	25.06.1929	LeCoultre & Cie	Covered barrel (19‴ LEC).
CH	141 607 b	06.09.1929	LeCoultre & Cie	Chronoflight.
CH	157 094	25.04.1930	Et. Ed. Jaeger SA	Watch with protective shutter.

LeCoultre demonstrated such a high technical level that it was judged "outside of the competition" at the Paris Universal Exhibition in 1900.

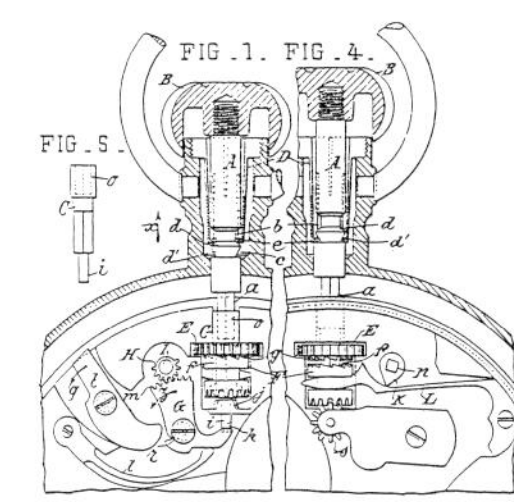

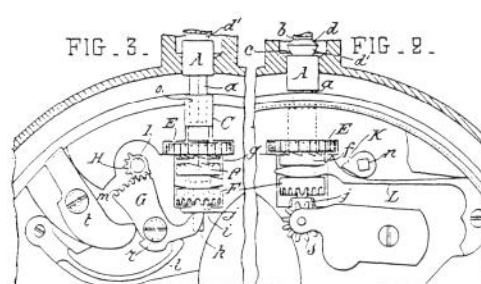

Patent N° CH 11 661 a

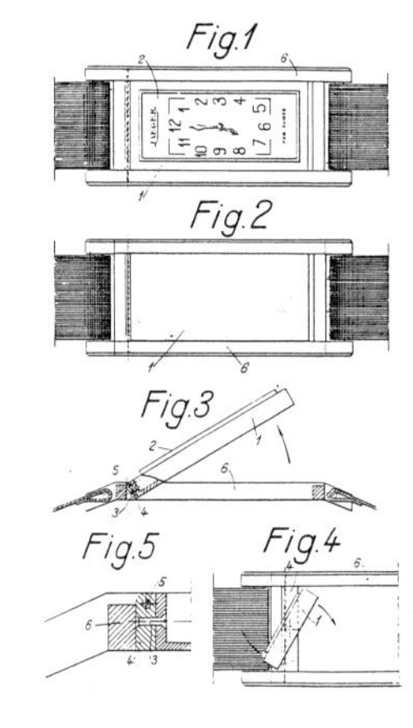

Patent N° CH 159 446

CH	155 514	05.02.1931	Et. Ed. Jaeger SA	Watch case.
CH	162 506	21.02.1931	Et. Ed. Jaeger SA	Watch-bracelet.
F	712 868 I	04.03.1931	(R.A. Chauvot)	Reverso patent.
UK	365 884 I	31.03.1931	(Gowland)	Ados table clock.
F	40 330	27.05.1931	(R.A. Chauvot)	1st suppl. to patent 712 868.
CH	159 446	06.07.1931	Et. Ed. Jaeger SA	Swivel watch.
CH	156 831	03.08.1931	Et. Ed. Jaeger SA	Rigid bracelet.
CH	164 612	11.11.1931	Et. Ed. Jaeger SA	Lug.
F	41 060	21.11.1931	(R.A. Chauvot)	2nd suppl. to patent 712 868.
CH	163 057	09.03.1932	Et. Ed. Jaeger SA	Table clock with multiple mobile dials.
CH	162 786 g	01.06.1932	LeCoultre & Cie	Power reserve.
CH	162 787	01.07.1932	Spécialités Horlo. SA	Flip-over watch.
CH	165 572	06.10.1932	Et. Ed. Jaeger	Attachment of linking bracelet.
CH	166 270 a	13.03.1933	LeCoultre & Cie	GH auto rewinding and time-setting.
CH	168 883 n	25.03.1933	LeCoultre & Cie	Time totaliser.
CH	177 477 a	07.02.1934	LeCoultre & Cie	Suppl. 166 270.
CH	181 295	26.02.1934	Et. Ed. Jaeger	Mystérieuse table clock.
CH	182 767	23.03.1934	Et. Ed. Jaeger	Watch case.
CH	185 462	28.08.1934	Et. Ed. Jaeger	Table clock with multiple dials.
CH	181 002	08.10.1934	Et. Ed. Jaeger	Watch with protective case.
F	817 956	22.05.1936	(J.L. Reutter)	Atmos II motor.
CH	202 280	28.01.1937	Et. Ed. Jaeger	Watch-bracelet.
CH	204 910	06.04.1937	Et. Ed. Jaeger	Watch with gaseous fluid.
CH	198 192	25.05.1937	Et. Ed. Jaeger	Mystérieuse table clock.
CH	202 028	17.01.1938	Et. Ed. Jaeger	Safety attachment for bracelet.
CH	208.025 b	19.11.1938	LeCoultre & Cie	Non-concentric hour, minute and chrono hands.
CH	206 229	27.03.1939	Et. Ed. Jaeger	8-day movement.
CH	206 763	29.03.1939	Et. Ed. Jaeger	8-day chronograph movement with 24-hour indication.
CH	213 779	11.04.1939	Et. Ed. Jaeger	Bracelet.
CH	215 270 n	31.08.1940	LeCoultre & Cie	Cycle counter.
CH	239 784	11.12.1941	Et. Ed. Jaeger	Watch case.
CH	217 010	16.01.1942	Société de vente JLC	Watch that can be folded away in slot.
CH	237 997	09.04.1942	Et. Ed. Jaeger SA	Wristwatch with plastic caseband.
CH	228 724	22.04.1942	Jaeger-LeCoultre	Metal bracelet.
CH	241 711	07.08.1942	Et. Ed. Jaeger SA	Disposition of gear-train in a watch movement.

CH	233 245	30.03.1943	Jaeger-LeCoultre	Bracelet.
CH	250 574	30.06.1944	Et. Ed. Jaeger	Bracelet clasp.
CH	257 783	16.02.1945	Et. Ed. Jaeger	Watch with transparent ring.
CH	269 232 h	05.06.1947	LeCoultre & Cie	Balance protection.
CH	273 456	23.06.1947	Et. Ed. Jaeger	Bracelet lug.
CH	274 904	23.06.1947	Et. Ed. Jaeger	Wristwatch with removable case.
CH	260 356 g	11.09.1947	LeCoultre + Zodiac	Power reserve.
CH	263 707 g	04.10.1947	LeCoultre + Zodiac	Power reserve.
CH	268 080 g	27.11.1947	LeCoultre + Zodiac	Suppl. 263 707.
CH	274 907 e+l	23.11.1948	LeCoultre & Cie	Alarm watch.
CH	281 488	02.05.1949	SAPIC	Manufacturing process for pin-wheels.
CH	281 188	02.09.1949	SAPIC	Pallet for horological movements.
CH	284 490	28.09.1949	SAPIC	Balance for horological movements.
CH	280 561 e+k	18.10.1949	LeCoultre & Cie	Alarm watch.
CH	290 358	29.03.1950	Et. Ed. Jaeger SA	Mystérieuse table clock.
CH	286 915	07.06.1950	Et. Ed. Jaeger SA	Self-winding device.
CH	286 915 f	07.06.1950	H. Rodanet	Runner-mounted rotor.
CH	285 846 e+k	18.07.1950	LeCoultre & Cie	Alarm indicator in aperture.
CH	287 929 f	18.07.1950	LeCoultre & Cie	External weight.
CH	287 613 f+a	21.08.1950	(F. Reymond)	Cal. 497 time-setting.
CH	287 930 f	14.09.1950	(F. Reymond)	Cal. 497 weight and power reserve.
CH	287 931f	14.09.1950	(F. Reymond)	Cal. 497 weight.
CH	287 939 e+g	15.12.1950	LeCoultre & Cie	Repeater alarm release.
CH	288 211 b	15.12.1950	LeCoultre & Cie	Simplified chronograph.
CH	291 880	13.03.1951	Et. Ed. Jaeger SA	Bracelet clasp.
CH	308 025	04.06.1951	Et. Ed. Jaeger SA	Device for limiting going-barrel torque.
CH	292 141 d+k	01.08.1951	LeCoultre & Cie	Calendar display.
CH	296 072 d	08.02.1952	LeCoultre & Cie	Calendar carrier.
CH	306 437	15.02.1952	Et. Ed. Jaeger SA	Extendable bracelet.
CH	308. 025 n	13.05.1952	(Ed. Jaeger)	Torque limiter.
CH	301 019 f	05.08.1952	F. Reymond	Cal. 812 pivot mass.
CH	308 039 e+f	15.01.1953	F. Reymond	Weight for automatic alarm.
CH	340 784	20.07.1956	Et. Ed. Jaeger SA	Shock-absorbing bearing-block for precision mechanism.
CH	335 182 d	09.05.1957	M. Audemars +	Calendar disk block.
CH	340 196 e+k	28.06.1957	R. Lebet	Alarm and parking mechanism.
CH	340 190 e+k	04.07.1957	R. Lebet	Time-zones and alarm indicator.
CH	351 223	05.08.1957	Et. Ed. Jaeger SA	Time-setting mechanism for multiple time indications.

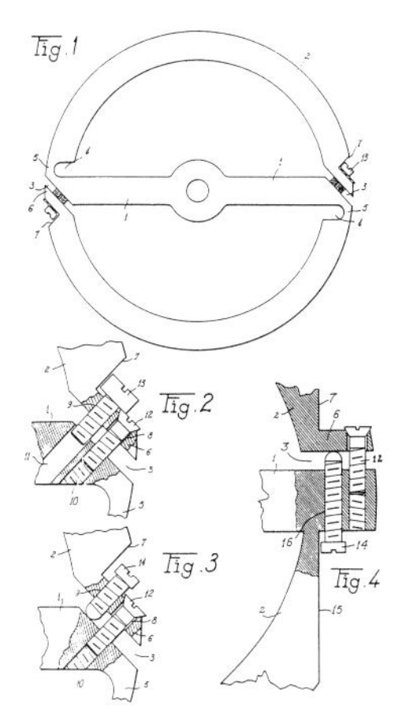

Patent N° CH 284 490

CH	338 764 f	17.05.1958	D. Fauconnet	Automatic bearings.
CH	343 294 f	28.10.1958	M. Audemars	Reverser pivot.
CH	343 295 f	28.10.1958	F. Reymond +	Runner weight pivot.
CH	343 288 n	30.10.1958	R. Lebet	Anti-dust cap.
CH	357 347 g	21.09.1959	J. Lebet	Music-box release.
F	1262622	19.04.1960	Et. Ed. Jaeger SA	Coin-watch.
CH	374 935 h+j	09.09.1960	J. Lebet	Balance for ultra-flat movement.
CH	377 732 j	09.09.1960	J. Lebet	Ultra-flat movement.
CH	377 725 a	14.12.1961	J. Lebet +	Winding shaft underside.
CH	378 233 e	14.12.1961	M. Grimm +	8-shiming alarm, cal. 240.
CH	385 746 g	14.12.1961	J.-P. Buttex	24-hour display.
F	1434205	14.01.1965	Et. Ed. Jaeger SA	Procedure for fixing balance-spring.
F	1462999	16.07.1965	Et. Ed. Jaeger SA	Device for adjusting bracelets with folding buckle.
CH	454 751 f	18.10.1965	M. Audemars	Weight pivot, cal. 920.
CH	427 365 n	28.10.1965	M. Berney	Drum display.
CH	508 930	18.04.1966	Et. Ed. Jaeger SA	Perfecting electric watch escapements with motor balance.
F	1544868	29.09.1967	Et. Ed. Jaeger SA	Instant date jump mechanism.
CH	517 960	20.12.1967	Et. Ed. Jaeger SA	Fixing key for balance-springs.
CH	514 881 g	20.10.1969	F. Jurado	Electric chime release.
CH	523 527 e+f	09.04.1970	M. Audemars +	Basic construction, cal. 916.
CH	560 413 d	09.11.1972	J. Lebet	Day-date mechanism.
CH	592 528 n	22.12.1975	C. A. Reymondin	Clips mechanism.
CH	635 537 n	17.04.1980	P. A. Meylan +	Pen top.
DE	3600590 m	11.01.1986	D. Wild	Bracelet.
DE	3732920 m	30.09.1987	D. Wild	Bracelet.
DE	3917636 e+l	31.05.1989	D. Wild	Alarm bell.
EP	400 207	03.10.1989	D. Wild	Bolting pushpiece.
DE	3917635	03.10.1989	D. Wild	Bracelet fastening.
DE	4010837	04.04.1990	D. Wild	Rotating bezel positioning.
EP	426 941	07.06.1990	D. Wild	Release pushpiece.
DE	4023033	20.07.1990	R. Billmann	Bracelet.
DE	4127825	22.08.1991	R. Guignard	Date indicator.
DE	4209082	20.03.1992	J. Lebet	Analog date.
DE	4322471	05.01.1994	R. Meis & J.-C. Meylan	Duo.
DE	19729903 A1	14.01.1999	D. Wild	Adjustable clasp.
		Patent pending	D. Wild	Bracelet adjusting device.

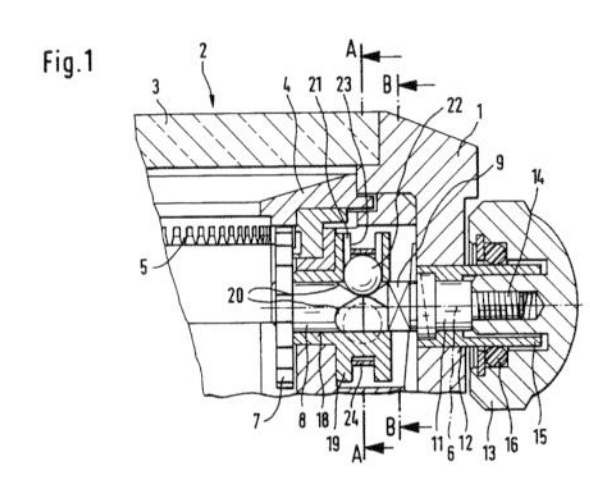

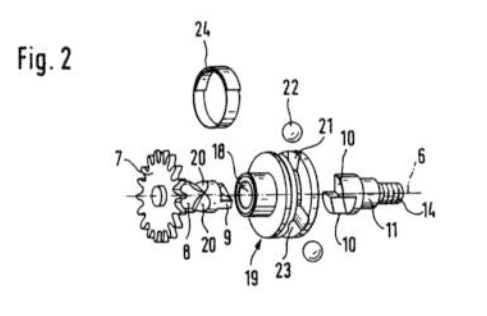

Patent N° DE 40 10 837

"Walking in the footprints of time. Driven by the past towards the future, we move through the present by giving shape to the moment. Second after second, minute after minute, we mark the cadence of the linearity which gives ceaseless rhythm to the world, and our mechanisms become visionary incarnations of this constant evolution." Each new movement developed by the master design-engineers of the Manufacture reflects a part of the future in the perpetual forward flight of time.

SUN
SAT
MON
FRI
TUE
THU
WED
AUG
JUL
JUN
MAY
SEP
APR
OCT
MAR
NOV
FEB
DEC
JAN
CAIRO
LONDON
PARIS
GMT
AZORES

II

The aesthetics of time

Movements of the Manufacture

The aesthetics of time

Hand, eye and heart represent our watchmakers' most precious tools.

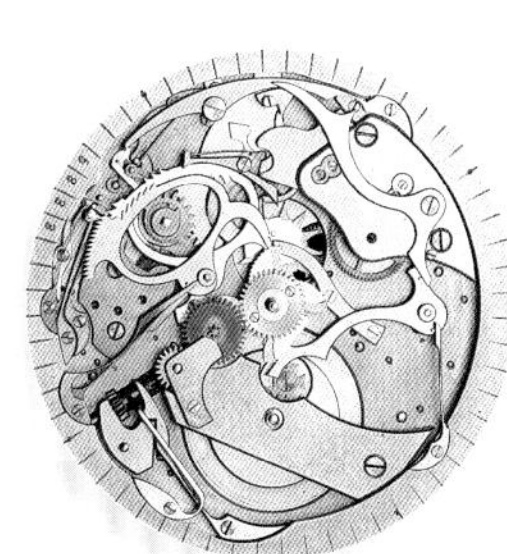

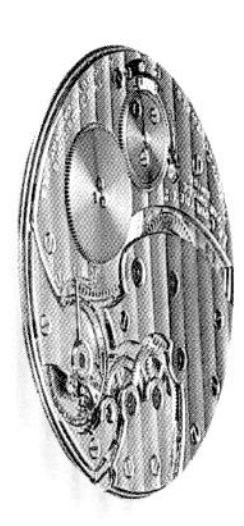

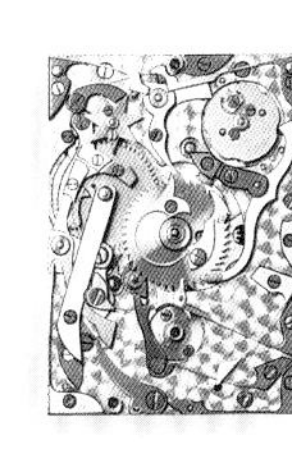

Watch connoisseurs hold Jaeger-LeCoultre in high regard because they know it makes the entire watch in its own workshops in the heart of Switzerland's watchmaking country. It is this authenticity that is so highly valued by collectors, who regard Jaeger-LeCoultre's timepieces as the standard by which fine watchmaking is judged.

Late 19th century. Movement for an ultra-thin minute-repeater pocket-watch.

At 1.38 mm, the wafer-thin pocket-watch movement of 1903 remains unsurpassed.

The first complicated Reverso, a prototype in 1937, featured a perpetual calendar with retrograde indicator.

The Manufacture in Le Sentier is home to the finest craftsmanship and to the most advanced precision machine-tools. Mechanical concepts take shape in computer-aided designs. Tiny, complicated parts are meticulously finished, assembled and adjusted into a movement by master-watchmakers. Watchmakers take immense pride in working for Jaeger-LeCoultre. They know that the company's insistence on the top standards of craftsmanship and its investment in training increase the status of their art. Another sign of authentic watchmaking is Jaeger-LeCoultre's habit of making movements that fit a specific watch-case, recalling the days when movements were individually made to fit pocket-watch cases. The fitted rectangular calibres

In the late 19th century, LeCoultre produced the Calibre N° 3 HPV movement in different sizes to fit each watch-case exactly.

The 1929 Calibre 101 remains the world's smallest mechanical watch movement.

1983. Calibre 608. Small high-tech quartz movement developed by Jaeger-LeCoultre.

1992. Calibre 822AD. This openworked movement, adorned with voluptuous Art Nouveau styling, is highly sought after by connoisseurs of fine watchmaking.

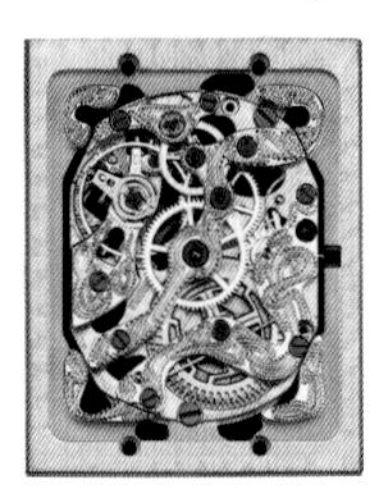

for the Reverso watches are thus rare. Jaeger-LeCoultre displays the unique ability to make rectangular movements with the most sought-after mechanical complications.
The Manufacture has developed and built some 250 movements since 1833. Today, it produces a larger variety of calibres than other manufacturers – 38 in all.
Its watchmaking repertoire ranges from Calibre 101, still the world's tiniest mechanical movement, to the great horological complications – tourbillons, perpetual calendars, moon-phases, minute-repeaters, power-reserve indicators, chronographs, alarms and watches with multiple time-zones.
Many of these timepieces are decorated by the few craftsmen who still know the arts of engraving, enamelling, gemsetting and chasing skeleton movements.
Jaeger-LeCoultre has chosen to make entire watch-movements and their cases in its own way, jealously safeguarding its reputation as the reference in fine Swiss watchmaking.

Different types of movements are denoted by the following abbreviations:

(A) Mechanical with automatic winding.
(M) Mechanical with manual winding.
(Q) Quartz.

"Taking time, waiting for it, or keeping ahead of it: this philosophy enriches us with a precious degree of humility. Acknowledging that time shapes an individual enables us to appreciate each manifestation of this supreme power. Restoring the beauty of vintage timekeepers, ensuring the smooth operation of new creations: such is our beautiful and precious task." Efisio Pintus, Mario and Luigi Manco are the guardians of time, which they maintain with unfailing perseverance.

Jaeger-LeCoultre
makes rectangular
movements to
fit the case shape

Rectangular movements

are very rare, and most rectangular watches nowadays are fitted with traditional round movements. Jaeger-LeCoultre continues to create special calibres perfectly adapted to each case.
A remarkable example: the movement of the Reverso Platinum Number One, the first entirely openworked calibre, created exclusively to reveal the prodigious mechanism of the legendary swivel watch.

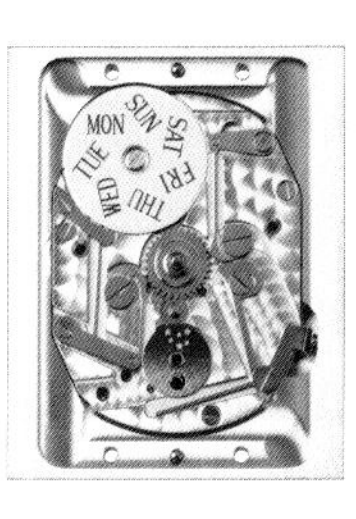

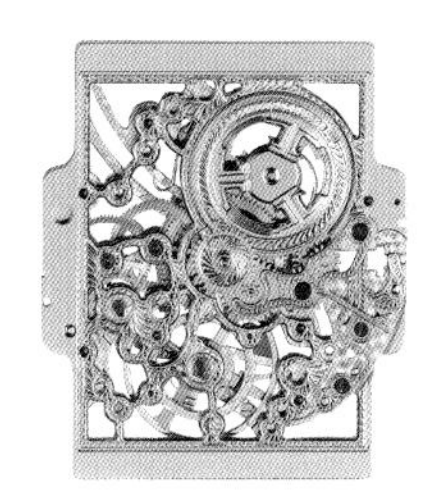

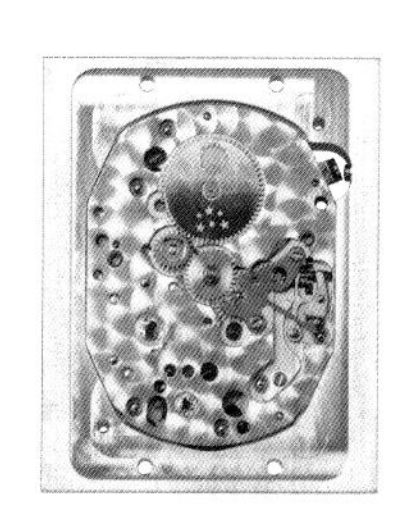

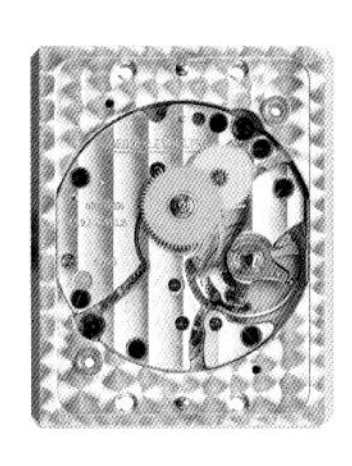

Calibre 835.
2001.
Mechanical manually-wound movement with small seconds, day disc, date by pointer in the centre, and day/night indication.
21,600 v/h,
21 jewels,
167 parts,
4.14 mm high.

Calibre 849R-SQ.
2001.
Mechanical manually-wound ultra-thin movement. Openworked and hand-engraved decoration in the Grecian Art style.
21,600 v/h,
19 jewels,
128 parts,
1.85 mm high.

Calibre 864.
2001.
Mechanical manually-wound movement with two time-zones and two day/night indications.
21,600 v/h,
19 jewels,
180 parts,
3.45 mm high.

Calibre 854J.
2001.
Mechanical manually-wound movement with two time-zones and day/night indication.
21,600 v/h,
22 jewels,
185 parts,
3.8 mm high.

Calibre 865.
2000.
Mechanical manually-wound movement indicating time on both sides with small seconds on the front.
21,600 v/h,
19 jewels,
130 parts,
3.45 mm high.

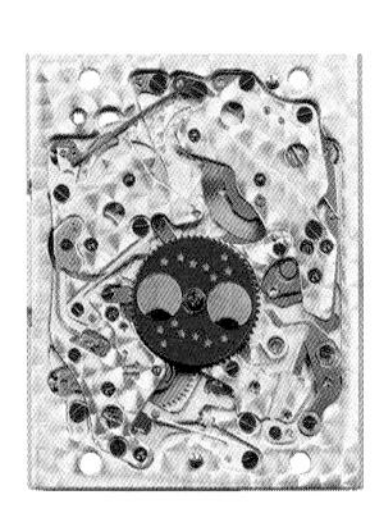

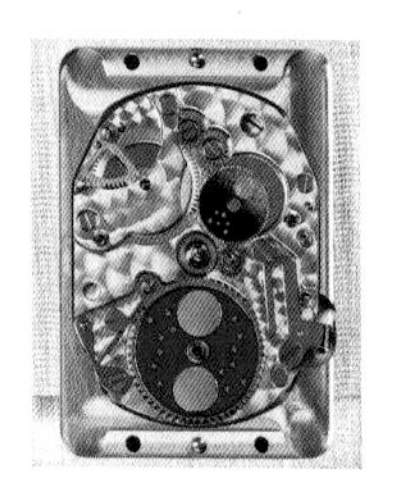

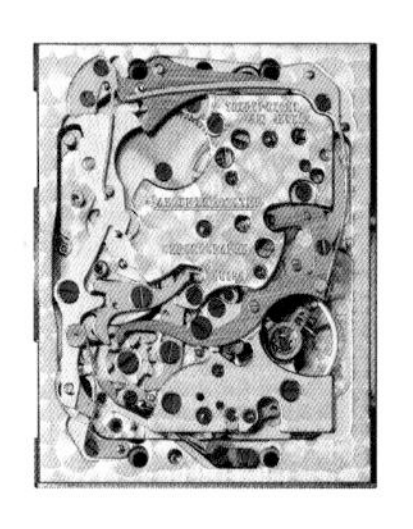

Calibre 855.
2000.
Mechanical manually-wound movement with perpetual calendar and moon phase.
21,600 v/h, 39 jewels, 276 parts, 4.3 mm high.

Calibre 823.
1999.
Mechanical manually-wound movement with power-reserve and small seconds. Day/night and moon-phase indications.
21,600 v/h, 23 jewels, 212 parts, 4.14 mm high.

Calibre 960R.
1998.
Mechanical automatic movement with centre seconds and date.
28,800 v/h, 31 jewels, 226 parts, 4.2 mm high.

Calibre 859.
1998.
Mechanical manually-wound movement with retrograde chronograph function, centre seconds and date.
28,800 v/h, 38 jewels, 317 parts, 4.5 mm high.

Calibre 858.
1998.
Mechanical manually-wound movement with two time-zones, 24-city display, GMT+/– and a day/night indication on front and back.
21,600 v/h, 22 jewels, 206 parts, 3.8 mm high.

Calibre 836.
1997.
Mechanical manually-wound movement with small seconds, day disc and date by pointer.
21,600 v/h, 21 jewels, 163 parts, 4.14 mm high.

Calibre 844.
1997.
Mechanical manually-wound movement indicating time on both sides.
21,600 v/h, 18 jewels, 100 parts, 3.45 mm high.

Calibre 829.
1996.
Mechanical manually-wound movement with retrograde chronograph function.
28,800 v/h, 36 jewels, 317 parts, 4.5 mm high.

Calibre 943.
1994.
Mechanical manually-wound movement striking the hours, quarters and minutes on two gongs.
21,600 v/h, 38 jewels, 306 parts, 4.85 mm high.

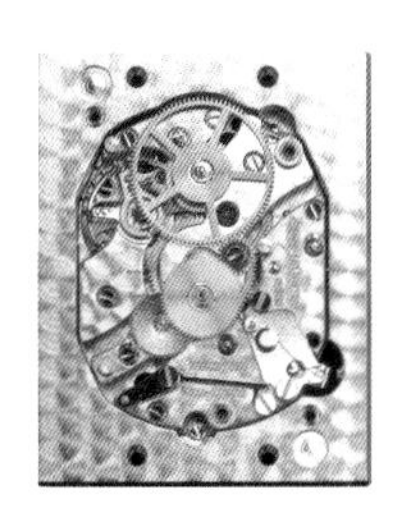

Calibre 854.
1994.
Mechanical manually-wound movement with two time-zones.
21,600 v/h, 21 jewels, 180 parts, 3.8 mm high.

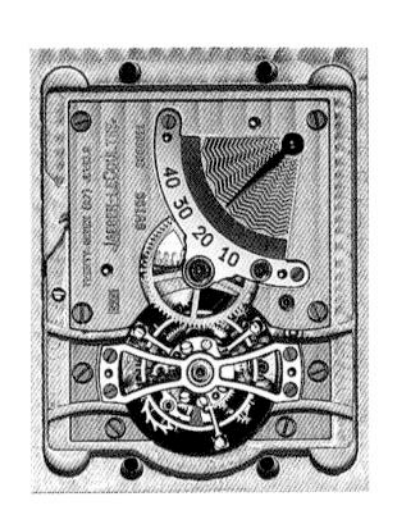

Calibre 828. 1993.
Mechanical manually-wound tourbillon movement with power-reserve indicator.
21,600 v/h, 27 jewels, 194 parts, 4.79 mm high.

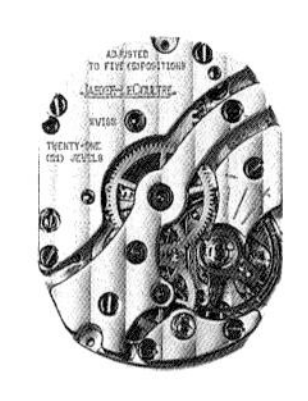

Calibre 822. 1992.
Mechanical manually-wound movement with small seconds.
21,600 v/h, 21 jewels, 134 parts, 2.94 mm high.

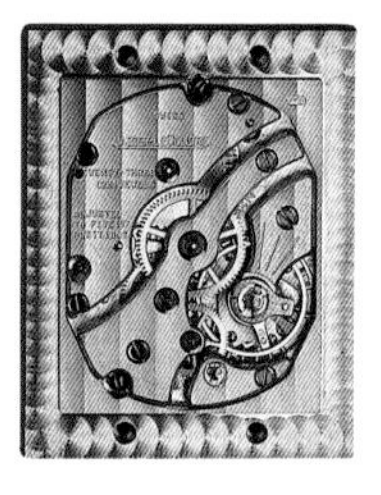

Calibre 824. 1991.
Mechanical manually-wound movement in gold with power-reserve indicator and date by pointer.
18,000 v/h, 23 jewels, 193 parts, 4.14 mm high.

Calibre 846. 1975.
Mechanical manually-wound movement.
21,600 v/h, 18 jewels, 93 parts, 2.9 mm high.

Calibre 101. 1929.
The world's smallest mechanical manually-wound movement.
21,600 v/h, 19 jewels, 98 parts, 3.4 mm high.

Movements
in a circle, from
pocket-watches
to wristwatches

Round movements

The circle is the obvious shape
for any mechanism that makes time
go round. The round movement also
gives watchmakers their finest
opportunity to incorporate smoothly
running additional complications
into the smallest possible space.
This is the very essence of watchmaking,
brilliantly illustrated in the ingenious
mechanism of the Master Geographic
created by Jaeger-LeCoultre in 1996:
this multiple time-zone movement allows
you to circle the globe.

**Calibre 909.
2000.**
Mechanical
automatic
movement
with perpetual
calendar and
mechanical
alarm striking
on a gong.
*28,800 v/h,
36 jewels,
349 parts,
8.3 mm high.*

**Calibre
891/448/2.
1997.**
Mechanical
automatic
movement with
day, date, month,
moon phase and
small seconds.
*28,800 v/h,
36 jewels,
275 parts,
5.53 mm high.*

**Calibre
889/440/2.
1996.**
Mechanical
automatic
movement
with perpetual
calendar and
moon phase.
*28,800 v/h,
50 jewels,
277 parts,
4.55 mm high.*

**Calibre 929/3.
1996.**
Mechanical
automatic
movement
with date,
power-reserve
indicator,
a 24-hour
second time-
zone and
day/night
indication.
*28,800 v/h,
38 jewels,
293 parts,
4.85 mm high.*

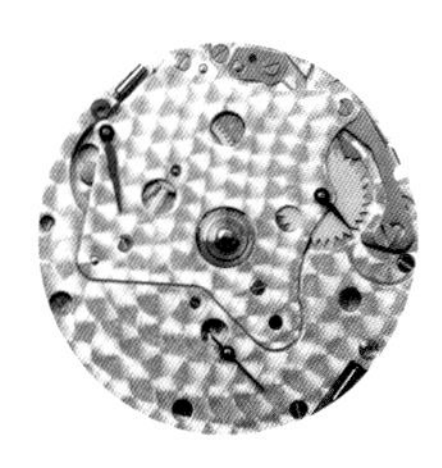

Calibre 849.
1994.
Mechanical manually-wound, ultra-thin movement.
21,600 v/h,
19 jewels,
123 parts,
1.85 mm high.

Calibre 889/2.
1994.
Mechanical automatic movement with date and centre seconds.
28,800 v/h,
36 jewels,
202 parts,
3.25 mm high.

Calibre 918.
1994.
Mechanical automatic movement with date, centre seconds and mechanical alarm, incorporating a gong.
28,800 v/h,
22 jewels,
260 parts,
7.45 mm high.

Calibre 891/447.
1993.
Mechanical automatic movement with day, date, month and small seconds.
28,800 v/h,
36 jewels,
270 parts,
5.53 mm high.

Calibre 928.
1993.
Mechanical automatic movement with small seconds, date and power-reserve indication.
28,800 v/h,
45 jewels,
256 parts,
4.85 mm high.

III

Reverso

The enduring Art Deco classic

Reverso

The 30s were brimming with extravagant forms of behaviour: Josephine Baker rides through Paris on a carriage pulled by an ostrich.

Creating a watch capable of standing up to the sporting exploits of polo players? At the beginning of the 30s, this challenge set by British officers of the Indian colonial army gives rise to a legend: the Reverso is born.

The spirit of the times reflected in its architecture. New York's Chrysler building, like the Reverso, remains an enduring symbol of the Art Deco age.

The models which set the Reverso off in 1931 on its long and brilliant career.

The aftermath of First World War saw the end of an old order, and the roaring 20s kicked off with a radical new look in fashion, art, design and architecture.

Hairlines and hemlines were shorter. Jean Cocteau invented the "Shocking pink" for Elsa Schiaparelli. Cubism gave way to New Objectivity. Casual elegance became the look. And Le Corbusier's architecture began to challenge the great Art Deco buildings. Watchmakers are sensitive to style trends, and it was thus natural for Jaeger-LeCoultre to capture the spirit of the age. The Reverso wristwatch, introduced by the company in 1931, had just the right blend of clean lines and durability that made it a perfect sports accessory. In those hard-playing days, few dress watches could stand up to such elite sports as polo, skiing or the Mille Miglia road-race. The Reverso could do just that, because Jaeger-LeCoultre's designers had the idea of mounting the watch on a solid carriage so that it could be turned over to protect the glass and dial. It was the first watch to use its case-back as a shield. Essentially unchanged for more than 70 years, the Reverso continues to flourish both as a modern timepiece and as one of the few original Art Deco objects still in use. There is hardly a famous watch-brand that is not a victim of counterfeiters. In some circles, it is even

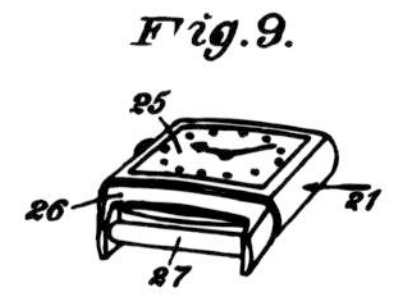

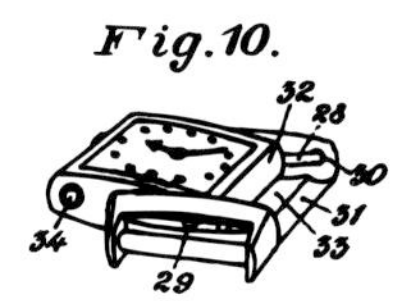

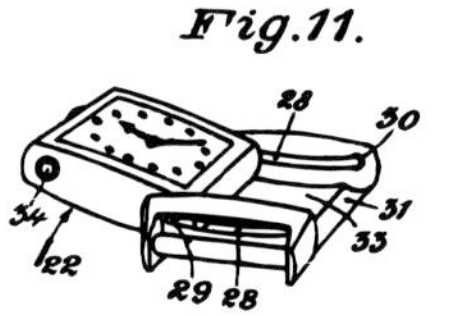

With more than 50 components, the Reverso case is one of the most complex on the market.

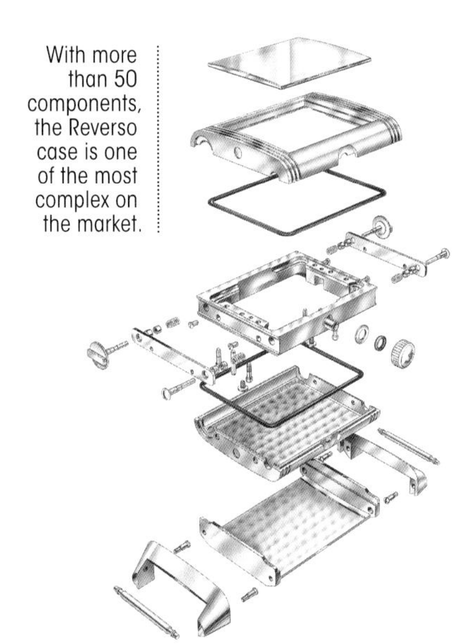

considered particularly chic to get hold of a cheap imitation that looks just like a genuine watch classic. However, the Reverso has never been successfully copied. Either the imitation is so inept that it gives itself away at first glance, or it is so perfect that it costs more to make than the real thing.
The original 1931 version of the complex Reverso case worked so well that it was manufactured unchanged for more than half a century. More recent advances in watchmaking, however, also made their influence felt in case-making; and, from 1985, an improved version of the Reverso case could be built. In 1998, the conception of the Reverso Gran'Sport was a landmark response to the demands of modern living. Its case, a genuine feat of elegance and water-resistance, is fully in tune with the development of modern leisure activities. Both cambered and pivoting, it features impeccable wearer

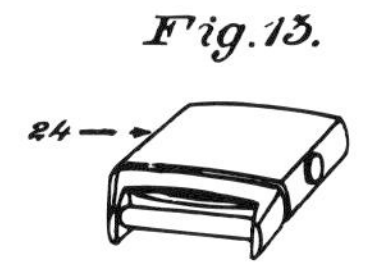

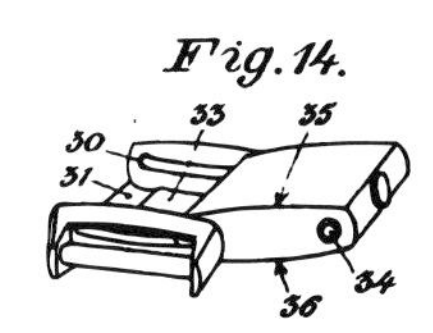

The turn of the century. The Reverso's swivel mechanism (as illustrated in the Swiss patent registration) has never been equalled by its imitators.

comfort and optimal security, while its ergonomic shape hugs the curve of the wrist and its exclusive blocking system prevents rotation when the watch is jarred. In terms of the feel of the metal bracelet, the Gran'Sport is fitted with an unprecedented and ingenious system: the curving links have been fashioned in metal and assembled one by one. Its clasp, made up of over fifty parts, is a technical masterpiece in its own right: its length adjustment system, as clever as it is easy to handle, simply makes light of changing seasons and temperatures. Yet another unique and patented system... A counterfeiter would have to create more than 50 separate parts to make even the simplest Reverso case. Each would have to be finished and fitted by hand so that the case rolls over smoothly for decades to come. Anything less than perfection would be immediately obvious.

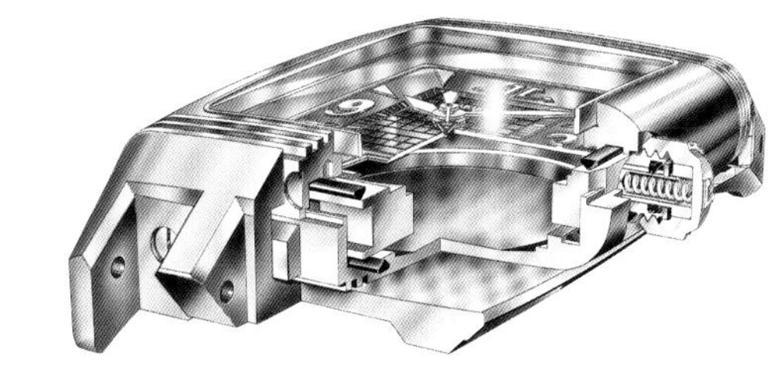

1998. With the Reverso Gran'Sport, the swivel case takes a more sporting turn. Water-resistant to 5 atm, it is fitted with a curved carrier that makes it particularly comfortable to wear.

The engraving

The other side of the Reverso

Engravings embellish the second face of the Reverso: an example of the superb decorative patterns created by the master-engravers of the Manufacture.

The Manufacture has developed a range of styles to inspire your choice. Your initials will be cut by the hand of a master-engraver (ask for our price list).

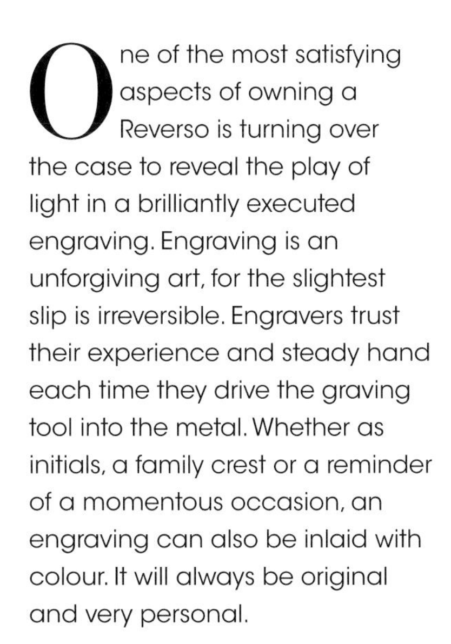

One of the most satisfying aspects of owning a Reverso is turning over the case to reveal the play of light in a brilliantly executed engraving. Engraving is an unforgiving art, for the slightest slip is irreversible. Engravers trust their experience and steady hand each time they drive the graving tool into the metal. Whether as initials, a family crest or a reminder of a momentous occasion, an engraving can also be inlaid with colour. It will always be original and very personal.

Anglaise

Impériale

Art Déco

Gothique

Belle Epoque

Gran'Sport

Miniatures in enamels

The other side of the Reverso

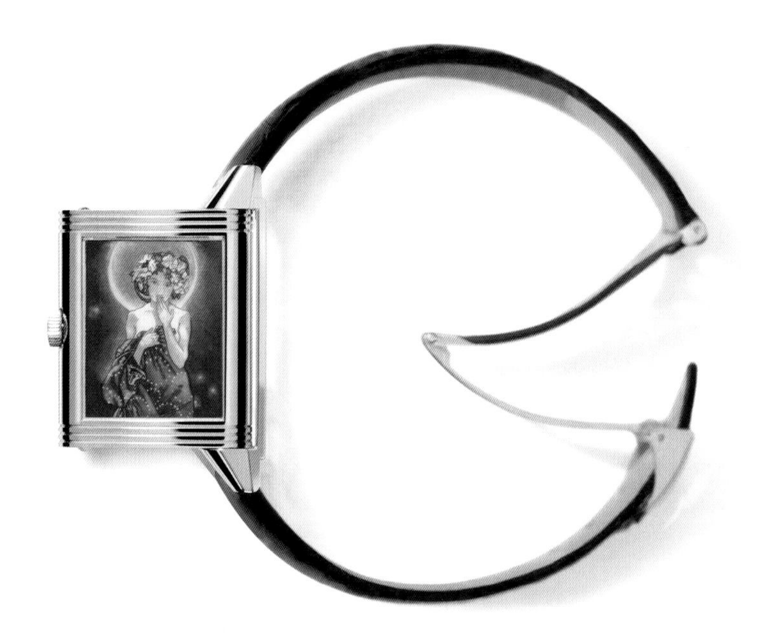

The real connoisseur may acquire the most intimate of all arts – a miniature painted in enamels. Such a Reverso gives its owner the absolute assurance of possessing a unique genuine watchmaking piece of art (here: Reverso "Clair de Lune").

Enthralled by the beauty of the Reverso, the Maharajah of Karputala ordered fifty of them enamelled with his effigy in 1932.

1996. Time moving to the rhythm of the seasons. Each has given rise to an enamelled miniature painting made especially for the Reverso by artist Miklos Merczel, who in this case has drawn inspiration from the Four Seasons by Alfons Mucha.

Of all types of painting, that of miniatures in enamel is the rarest and most precious. Art schools no longer have this subject in their curriculum, and it is increasingly difficult to find enamel colours of the traditional quality.

Jaeger-LeCoultre is particularly fortunate, therefore, in having among its specialists two of the few artists in enamel. Furthermore, they have access to a supply of proper enamel colours. The Manufacture is thus one of the last watchmakers able to offer this traditional high art of watch decoration. A miniature in enamel on a Reverso watch is one of the rarest art forms available today.

It takes several weeks of intense concentration to create a miniature. The art consists, literally, in playing with fire. It needs the nerves of a bomb-disposal expert, an eye-surgeon's hand and, above all, plenty of time. The slightest

1996. "Winter": a snowy landscape delicately enshrouds the shivering lady. Draped in her cloak, she shields herself from the cold and protects herself from prying eyes. An all-encircling sensuality, marvellously recreated for this enamel miniature.

1899. At the turn of the century, Alfons Mucha painted "Aurore" and "Crépuscule" (literally, Dawn and Dusk) to illustrate humankind's fears of an unknown future. One figure covers her naked body at nightfall, and the other hesitates to disrobe as a new day dawns... The enamel Reverso echoes these uncertainties on the threshold of a new millennium.

1999. "Topaze". All the many authentic hues of gemstones are recreated through the ochre shades of the enamel. The splendid lady painted on this pocket-watch reflects the voluptuous Art Nouveau style of the work of Alfons Mucha.

miscalculation during the process ruins the entire work. First the gold case-back must be sandwiched between coatings of white enamel so that it does not buckle when fired in the oven heated to 850° C. Then the artist builds up the picture in layers of enamel colours, minutely painted with a brush pointed to a single hair. Each layer of enamel is vitrified by firing it for a precise time in a furnace. But the colours change when they are fired, so the artist has to calculate the chromatic shift and estimate the final tone. The colours are intensified in each layer until the final picture emerges in the virtuoso display of brilliance and colour that has always made a miniature in enamels the most treasured - and intimate - of possessions.

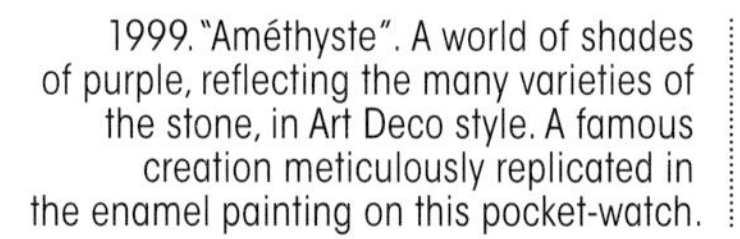

1999. "Améthyste". A world of shades of purple, reflecting the many varieties of the stone, in Art Deco style. A famous creation meticulously replicated in the enamel painting on this pocket-watch.

2000. A marvellous testimonial to Art Nouveau, the "Rubis" Montre de poche is a timekeeper worthy of our times. Enamel reproduction of a portrait by Alfons Mucha. White gold case set with brilliants and baguette diamonds.

The dial of the "Rubis" and "Emeraude" Reverso Montres de poche displays the hours, minutes and small seconds and features a thermometer and a power-reserve indication. Mechanical manually-wound movement, Calibre 823. Pictured below, the "Rubis" model.

2000. This exceptional timekeeper in white gold highlights the know-how of the master-enamellers at Jaeger-LeCoultre. "Emeraude", an enamel reproduction of a painting by Alfons Mucha, gives your time a truly unique dimension.

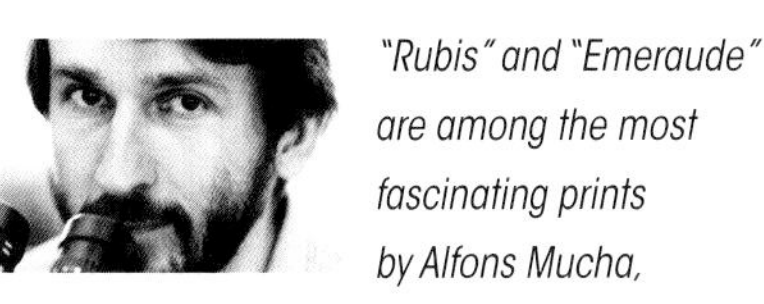

"Rubis" and "Emeraude" are among the most fascinating prints by Alfons Mucha, the famous Czech painter in the Art Nouveau style. A century later, they have given rise to two Reverso Montres de poche, featuring enamelled miniatures reproduced with the highest artistic faithfulness to the original. "First, we had to find the palette of shades inherent to each stone and to chose those which correspond to the choices made by Mucha. This was no easy task, since the colours of the original works had lost their vibrancy. We therefore accentuated the various hues of ruby and emerald to enable them to glow with their full radiance and express their symbolism."

Miklos Merczel / Master-enameller

The Reverso Email "Etoile du Matin"
and "Clair de Lune" are presented
and sold together in a limited series
of 25 sets in a precious wooden box.

Reverso "Clair de Lune".
Grand feu enamelled
dial and case-back.
18-carat yellow gold.
Crocodile strap with
yellow gold folding buckle.

276 14 02 (M)
Calibre 822.

Reverso "Etoile du Matin".
Grand feu enamelled
dial and case-back.
18-carat yellow gold.
Crocodile strap with
yellow gold folding buckle.

276 14 01 (M)
Calibre 822.

"The dance of shapes and colours, gently cradled by time, form a landscape which awakens our innermost feelings. It is as if nature was staging a fabulous show in which we are both actors and spectators. The admiring painter captures one moment of this performance and carefully frames it within a picture. The enameller scrupulously reinterprets the scene into a miniature mosaic." It is thus that Sophie Roche and Miklos Merczel revive the finest prints of all time on the receptive back of Reverso watches.

Precious stones

The other side of the Reverso

The unique pivoting case, reversible at a touch, provides a precious double canvas on which our master-jewellers create sparkling works of art in precious stones.

With its leaf patterns adorned with pastel blue sapphires, the Reverso Florale Feuilles is an ode to time. The refinement of its scrolling motif continues from one side of the case to the other and the masterful gem-setting inevitably catches and holds the observer's attention.

What better vehicle could one provide for the earth's rich mineral wealth than the swivel case of the Reverso? Uniquely valuable thanks to its turn-over concept, it lends itself to a fascinating duality that represents an infinite source of creativity for the master-jewellers and gem-setters of the Manufacture.

The rotating case of the Reverso is a worthy setting for earth's noblest minerals – diamonds, rubies, emeralds and sapphires. But gemstones were the last thing the original designers had in mind when they devised the famous swivel case for polo-players. The case fit so exactly on its carrier-plate that there was no room for gem-setters to exercise their art. The Manufacture's case-makers came to their rescue with a special model designed to secure and reveal the four great precious stones in all their splendour. Technically, it is a rare version of a rare timepiece. Artistically, it is unique.

The back of a Reverso Montre de poche lends itself to the most varied types of engraving. In this case, the enamelled diamond-set monogram stands out beautifully against the ochre background, underscoring the harmonious contrasts between brilliants and yellow sapphires.

IV

Reverso Limited series

Reverso Limited series in pink gold

500 strokes of genius

Daniel Wild, Reverso 60ème.

Sylvain Golay, Reverso Tourbillon.

Eric Coudray, Reverso Répétition Minutes.

Manel Guérin, Reverso Chronographe.

Philippe Vandel, Reverso Géographique.

Rachel Torresani, Reverso Quantième Perpétuel.

The six Reverso Limited series in pink gold encapsulate all the talents exercised within the Manufacture. A succession of masterpieces orchestrated by the master-watchmakers and the case and movement design engineers.

In 1991, Jaeger-LeCoultre celebrated 60 years of success for the Reverso by opening up new horizons for this legendary model. Connoisseurs and collectors of prestige watchmaking were expecting a surprise: they were not disappointed in discovering the Reverso 60ème and its first-ever large-size case, fashioned in 18-carat pink gold in a limited edition of 500.

At the heart of a case somewhat larger than the original, it houses Calibre 824, a mechanical manually-wound movement featuring plates and bridges in 14-carat pink gold, that can be viewed through the sapphire crystal. In golden letters, the Grande Taille case was actually writing the first lines of a new chapter in Reverso history. The new variation was to become a fertile source of inspiration for many new feats. It enabled the master-watchmakers of the Manufacture to give shape to a challenge that had been a long-time dream: that of creating a Reverso with complications. Such was the genesis of the prodigious legend of the Reverso Limited series in 18-carat pink gold: six exceptional models crafted in series of just 500, always and only in the Grande Taille case. One after another, successive launches of the models in this prestigious lineage were to accompany collectors to the threshold of the new millennium. Two years after the creation of the Reverso 60ème, Jaeger-LeCoultre offered collectors the brilliant achievement of the rectangular tourbillon. Designed to cancel out the influence of gravity on the balance which regulates a watch, the tourbillon was first patented in 1801 and is still to this day the most refined mechanism in watchmaking history. The device consists of a mobile carriage

The Reverso 60ème reflects Jaeger-LeCoultre's technical mastery and inventiveness: on the front, its solid silver guilloché dial enhanced by Arabic numerals and the applied gilded JL logo displays the hours, minutes, small seconds at 6 o'clock, along with the date and power-reserve.

The 194 parts in the Reverso Tourbillon movement incorporate a power-reserve display. Calibre 828.

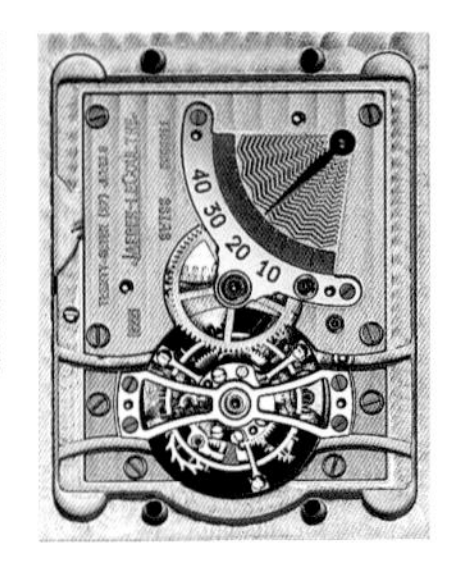

Those who know about watches will immediately recognize originality in the quality of the chime and the ribbed slide that sets it going. Calibre 943.

containing all the parts that are essential to the operation of a time-keeper. Completing a revolution every 60 seconds, it reduces the variations in rate due to gravity. Nestling at the heart of the Reverso Tourbillon, this rotating carriage made up of 70 parts weighs only 0.25 gram. Jaeger-LeCoultre Calibre 828, which made this feat possible, is a micromechanical marvel: rectangular and endowed with a power-reserve, it comprises 194 parts, each polished, chamfered and finished by hand, nestling within a volume of just 3 cm^3. To discover this masterpiece, one need only admire it through the transparent sapphire case-back. Sounding the time both night and day is a feat that the Reverso Répétition Minutes performs brilliantly. Initially designed to tell the time in the dark, these time-keepers chime on request the hours and quarters, along with the minutes. Their crystal-clear tone is produced by tiny hammers striking steel gongs when a bolt is slid along the side of the case. In 1994, in order to introduce the minute repeater mechanism within the rectangular movement of the Reverso, watchmakers and technicians developed Calibre 943. The shape of the gongs imposed by the case is remarkable and their acoustic quality has been meticulously researched to achieve purity and excellence. In 1996, the Reverso Chronographe Rétrograde brought together a maximum of functions within a minimum of space, thanks to the sophistication of Jaeger-LeCoultre Calibre 829. The front displays various time measurements: hours, minutes and date at 6 o'clock as well as the start/stop chronograph indication. The back is reserved for chronograph functions, with a 60-second counter and retrograde 30-minute counter. When the minute-counter hand

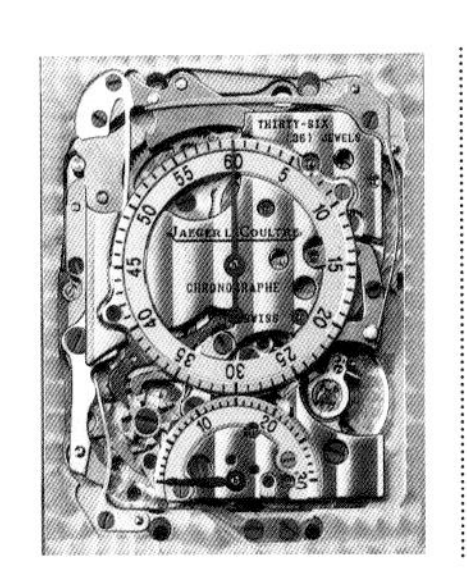

The work of the hammer-lever, the control-pawl and the jumper-spring of the column-wheel demonstrates the technical feat accomplished by Calibre 829 in order to integrate the chronograph functions.

The great ingenuity of Calibre 858 lies in enabling the time, city and day/night indications to remain perfectly synchronized, whichever city is chosen.

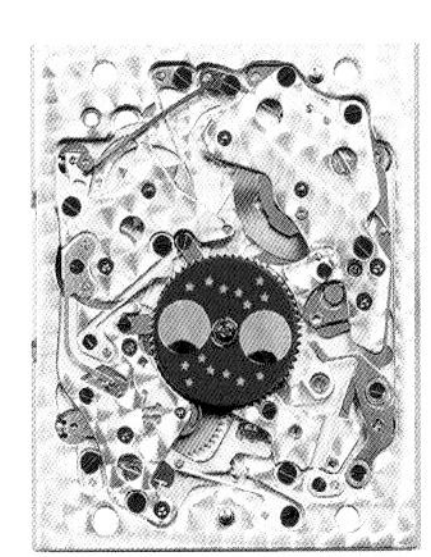

The main difficulty of Calibre 855 stems from the retrograde date display: synchronizing the retrograde date, day, month and moon-phase functions, and avoiding discrepancies in date between the months.

reaches half an hour, the retrograde counter automatically returns to zero before pursuing its course. The sapphire crystal allows one to admire this exemplary mechanism made up of 317 parts, which represent a technological breakthrough in terms of miniaturized time measurement. A precious invitation to travel, the Reverso Géographique explored uncharted territories in 1998: such a complication had never yet been fitted within a rectangular case. Made up of 206 parts, mechanical manually-wound Jaeger-LeCoultre Calibre 858 drives the multiple functions and the 24 time-zone indication. On the front, the hour, minute and small seconds at 6 o'clock are enhanced by a day/night aperture displaying the perpetual course of the sun and the stars. On the back, the hours and minutes in the second time-zone, along with a display of the selected city, are complemented by GMT +/– and day/night indications. Each city corresponds to one of the 24 time-zones: 12 in GMT + (East) and 12 in GMT – (West). Constituting a truly masterful creation, the Reverso Géographique ensures that the various indications are perfectly synchronized, whichever city is selected. The sixth and last edition of the Limited series in pink gold, the Reverso Quantième Perpétuel powered by Calibre 855, concluded the legend by presenting the most sophisticated useful complication of all Reverso watches. The front ticks off the time, with day/night indication and leap-year display. The back features the perpetual calendar functions: retrograde date, day, month and moon phases. As the new millennium unfolds, the Reverso Quantième Perpétuel raises the curtain on eternity…

Reverso 60ème.
1991.
Limited series
of 500.
Calibre 824.

Reverso Tourbillon.
1993.
Limited series
of 500.
Calibre 828.

Reverso Répétition
Minutes.
1994.
Limited series
of 500.
Calibre 943.

Reverso Chronographe
Rétrograde.
1996.
Limited series
of 500.
Calibre 829.

Reverso Géographique.
1998.
Limited series
of 500.
Calibre 858.

Reverso Quantième
Perpétuel.
2000.
Limited series
of 500.
Calibre 855.

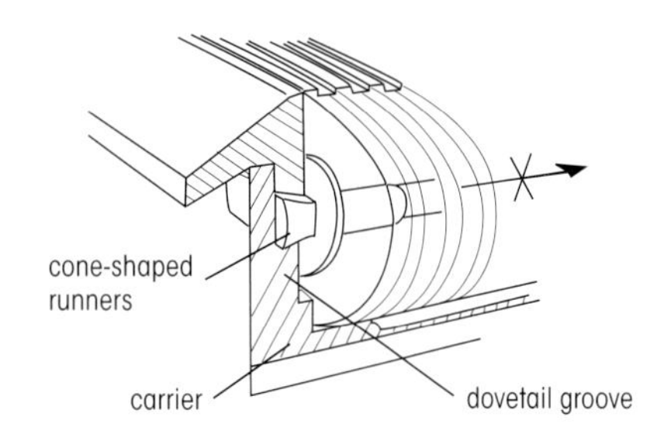

The runners that hold the case in its carrier have been modified for the Grande Taille case.

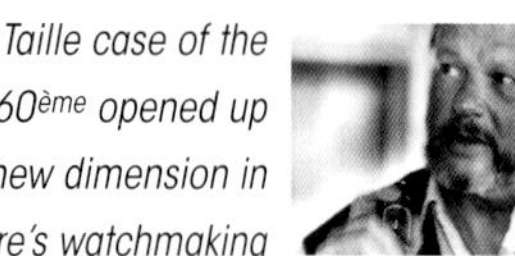

The Grande Taille case of the Reverso 60ème opened up a whole new dimension in Jaeger-LeCoultre's watchmaking technology: "Comprising over 50 parts, this case is one of the most complex ever designed. Finalised on the basis of technical plans before proceeding to production using high-precision machinery, it allowed us to fulfil a dream: that of making the Reverso the repository of the most beautiful watchmaking complications."

Daniel Wild / Design-engineer

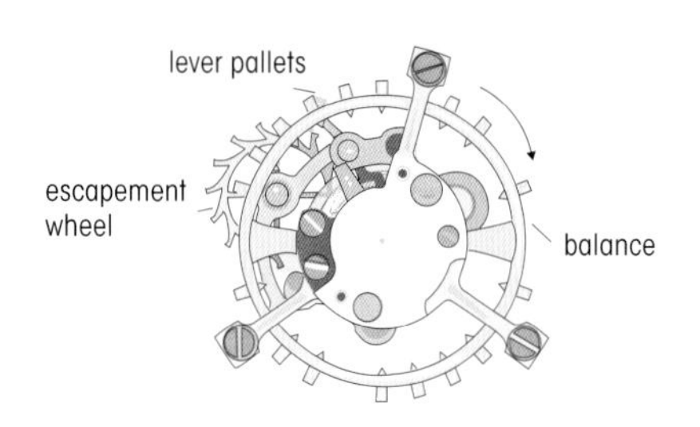

The tourbillon mechanism consists of a revolving carriage containing the balance, the lever pallets and the escapement wheel.

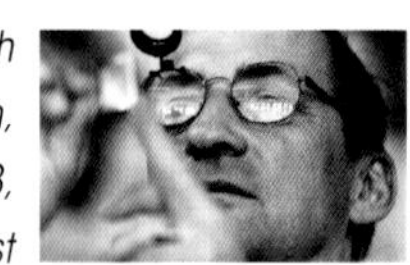

In order to endow the Reverso with the fascinating tourbillon mechanism, Jaeger-LeCoultre created Calibre 828, a micromechanical gem: "It is the first time a tourbillon has been incorporated within a rectangular movement. To achieve this, we have created a carriage which, by revolving once a minute around a fixed seconds-wheel, cancels out the negative effect of gravity. Composed of 70 parts, it nonetheless weighs only 0.25 gram. The conception of this movement as a whole constituted an unprecedented challenge in terms of miniaturisation: 3 cm^3 to assemble 218 parts, each polished, bevelled and finished by hand."

Sylvain Golay / Master-watchmaker

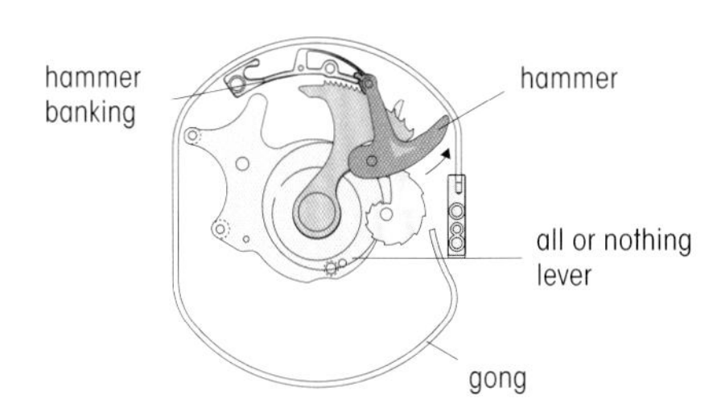

A hammer chimes the hours on a low-tone gong, the other strikes the minutes on the high-tone gong. Both hammers alternate to indicate the quarter-hours.

In addition to its purity and acoustic excellence, each detail of the Reverso Répétition Minutes mechanism has been honed to the extreme. "We had to equip Calibre 943 with a governor that keeps the chime sounding with the regularity of a metronome: that meant turning two pink gold weights on the strike-hammer, which are driven apart by centrifugal force and whose speed is curbed by two jewel runners."

Eric Coudray / Master-watchmaker

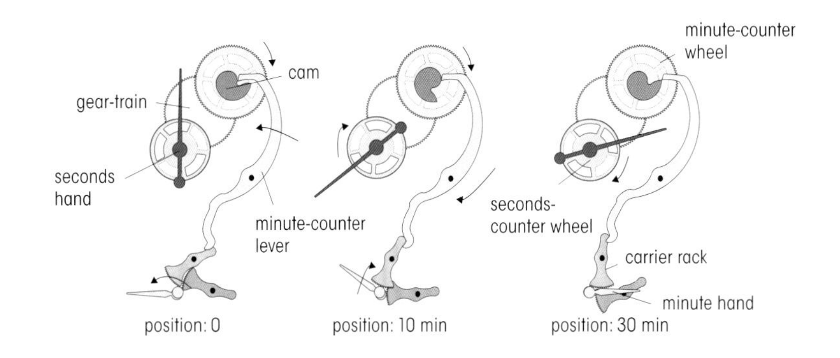

As the pivotal part of the chronograph mechanism, the cam driving the minute-counter called for extremely complex calculations.

The return-to-zero mechanism of the Reverso Chronographe Rétrograde required a precious sum of know-how: "Pressing the lower pushpiece releases the hammer which, while pushing against the heart-piece, returns the minute-counter wheel to zero. The latter in turn transmits the function to the opposite end of the movement thanks to an extremely complex principle based on a lever and spiral rack, which enables the minute-counter hand to return to its initial position."

Manel Guérin / Master-watchmaker

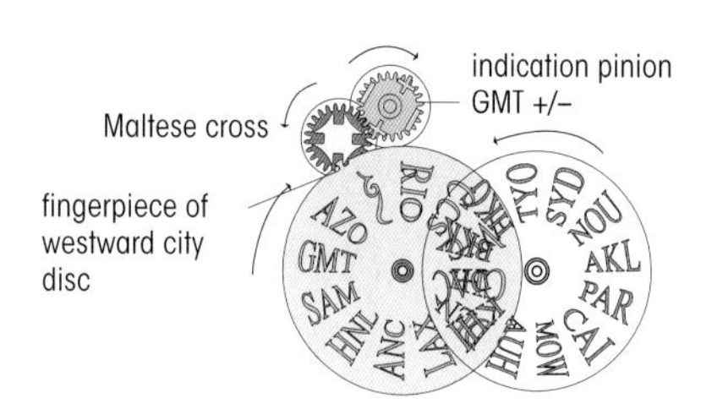

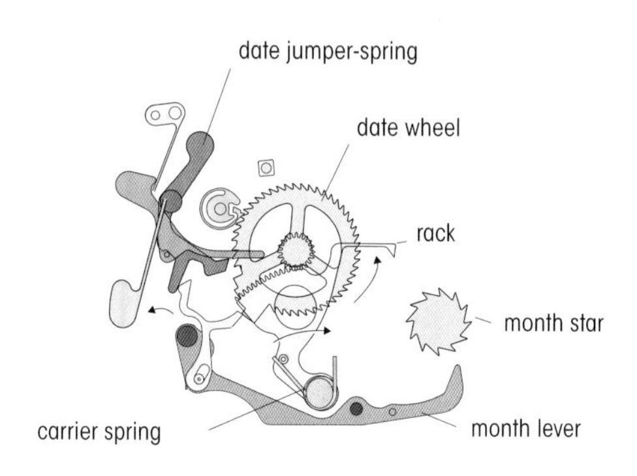

A single pushpiece enables simultaneous adjustment of the two city discs, by bringing the time-zone corrector fingerpiece back to its initial position.

The retrograde function at the end of the month is governed by the impulse from the rack-spring which pushes the date wheel back until it locks.

After 18 months of research, the design-engineer of the Reverso Géographique succeeded in housing its mechanism within a volume less than one millimetre high. But one enigma was yet to be resolved: "As the 12 time-zones moved past, the day/night indication no longer corresponded to the cities displayed: it was inverted. I therefore devised a mechanism enabling the hour, city and day/night indications to remain synchronized, whatever city was chosen. I added an aperture with the GMT +/– indication, so one could know to which town the day/night indication referred."

Philippe Vandel / Design-engineer

Fitting 276 parts into a rectangular case with an absolute minimum of volume: the Reverso Quantième Perpétuel takes horological miniaturization to its uttermost limits: "The main difficulty lay in the retrograde date display: achieving perfect synchronization of the date and months, and avoiding date rebounds when the retrograde mechanism was in operation."

Rachel Torresani / Design-engineer

"Nature, which gives cadence to time, is the point of reference for our creations. Our watch mechanisms are modelled on the aesthetics and balance of a flower: each component is vital to the regularity and harmony of the whole. Each watch therefore becomes a wonderful living organism, and human beings never grow tired of exploring its secrets." The workshop of Sylvain Golay, Angèle Mequies and Jacques Coulet is a bubbling think tank in which original ideas rise regularly to the surface.

Reverso Limited series in platinum

The arrival of a new dynasty

In 1931, the first swivel case found its place in the history of Jaeger-LeCoultre patents. 70 years on, the legend is more vibrantly alive than ever and proves that it still has the power to turn heads. For a master-watchmaker who devotes himself unstintingly to the passion of his craft, there are no limits to creativity. Hardly has he completed a masterpiece, than he sets off in pursuit of new complications and new challenges blending function, form and matter.

The creation of the first platinum case for the Reverso was a challenge that required the prototype makers to demonstrate great patience, rigorous attention and meticulous care. "Of all precious metals, platinum is the hardest of all to machine. It is impossible to use conventional cutting tools. The latter must be replaced by polycrystalline tools, or by means of spark erosion." Pascal Riat, Dominique Picht and Jacky Rochat - Prototype-makers.

This same inventive passion reigns supreme within the workshop nicknamed "the think tank" within the Manufacture Jaeger-LeCoultre. It is there that the project for a second dynasty of Reverso Limited series of 500 took shape. In homage to authenticity and nobility, platinum was chosen to clothe a new line of masterpieces. After the six prodigious complications in pink gold, successively launched between the 60th anniversary of the Reverso and the year 2000, the new collection of Limited series in platinum is opening up fascinating new vistas. Jaeger-LeCoultre's master-watchmakers have already focused all their know-how and imagination on preparing this new chapter in the art of complications... Every two years a new work of art and watchmaking expertise will become a fresh milestone in the legend of the six Reverso models in platinum. A thrilling appointment with the unusual for Reverso collectors and enthusiasts.

Reverso Platinum Number One

In this world of transparency devoted to the mechanisms of fine watchmaking, Reverso Platinum Number One reveals the secrets of its inner life.

The Reverso Art Déco reveals a strikingly beautiful mechanism. Adorned with the voluptuous grace of Art Nouveau, its movement carries us beyond function to a world where Haute Horlogerie and the decorative arts merge in perfect harmony.

1927. This pocket-watch reflects the attention Jaeger-LeCoultre has consistently devoted to the aesthetic appearance of its movements. Its openworked dial reveals the beauty of this grande complication. LeCoultre Calibre 17JSMCCRVQ N° 154 with minute repeater, 30-minute chronograph and instant perpetual calendar.

The Reverso Platinum Number One is a first. The first Reverso in platinum and the first openworked movement developed for the legendary swivel case. This watchmaking prodigy has chosen the most restrained of noble metals to enhance its inner life.

In order to give life and movement to the Reverso Platinum Number One, Calibre 849 has been transformed into a genuine work of art in its own right. In crafting the prestigious openworked manually-wound Calibre 849R-SQ, its creators succumbed to their penchant for aesthetics: they have infused it with the artistic refinement of a hand engraving inspired by Ancient Greece. In the workshop of the Vallée de Joux, 500 Reverso Platinum Number One watches are preparing to win the hearts of collectors the world over. Pared down to the essentials, the slender material of the plates and bridges enables the gaze to smoothly follow each function of the movement: the winding-mechanism and even the open barrel, held by the triple Jaeger-LeCoultre logo. There is no dial for this marvel of transparency.... which does not prevent it from displaying two faces, as one would expect from a Reverso! On the front, the blued steel hands are the only time indications, all remaining space being dedicated to the inner life of the watch and the art of its mechanical intricacies. In harmony with the purity of this watch-making quintessence, the Jaeger-LeCoultre emblem is placed on the decorated flange of the case. The Reverso Platinum Number One is the most daring and authentic incarnation of what the Reverso means to connoisseurs: a timeless value, loyal to its origins, which perpetuates the highest watchmaking traditions through successive eras.

Reverso Platinum Number One.
950 platinum.
Crocodile strap with platinum folding buckle.

216 64 01 (M)
Calibre 849R-SQ.
Limited series of 500.

"One could never grow tired of observing time as it passes. From dawn to dusk, each of its manifestations follows on in turn, designing and shaping the landscape like a constantly changing painting." To enable us to admire the slightest fractions of time in motion, Pascal Riat, Dominique Picht and Jacky Rochat have endowed the Reverso Platinum Number One with an unprecedented case, transparent from both sides.

NIGHT AND DAY
JAEGER-LECOULTRE
REVERSO
SWISS MADE
MAR
JAEGER-LECOULTRE
NIGHT AND DAY
SWISS
MADE
JAEGER-LECOULTRE
NIGHT
DAY

V

Reverso Specialities

Two faces for a unique perception of time

Reverso Specialities

Everything has two sides. Right from the start, this is particularly true for the Reverso, the quick change artist among watches. An elegant turn of thumb and index finger, letting the face of the watch disappear as if by magic and re-setting the case again with a little "click", satisfies curiosity and provides a little help in escaping the merciless dictates of time – Click.

With its larger case and, for the first time, a sapphire case-back that allows you to take a glance at the mechanism inside, Reverso as "re-invented" in 1991 represents a quantum leap. Hereafter it was possible to use the second side either for additional functions or as a "living" work of technical art.

The first example of this is the Reverso 60ème. Once begun, the process of expanding on this simple idea proved unstoppable.

Reverso Art Déco.
18-carat pink gold.
Calibre 822 Art Déco.

The Reverso window in the skies

Reverso Sun Moon

Whatever the weather (or the time), you will never lose sight of the course of the sun and moon.

In tribute to Jacques-David LeCoultre, who died in 1948, the watch bearing his name was launched a year later. Fitted with a calendar and moon-phase display, the "LeCoultre" houses manually-wound Calibre 486.

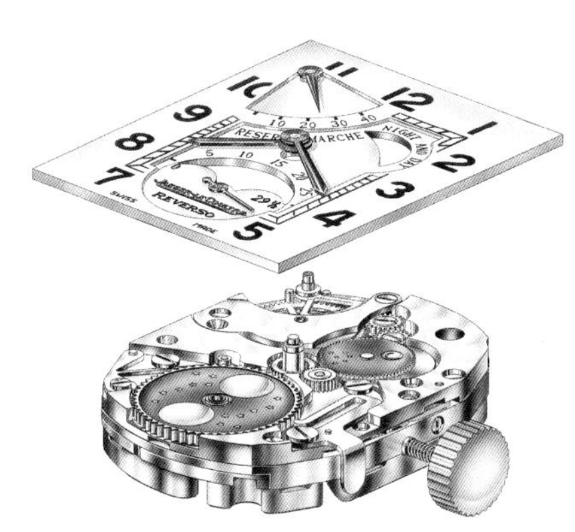

Is it noon or midnight? Wherever it finds itself, the Reverso Sun Moon never loses sight of the celestial bodies: its Calibre 823, made up of 212 parts, incorporates moon-phase and day/night display functions.

Recognizing the hidden face of the moon, distinguishing the diurnal phase from a nocturnal phase: the Reverso Sun Moon makes it possible to read the time as if through a window in the skies. Its Grande Taille case brings within orbit complications previously unknown to the Reverso.

Calibre 823, a mechanical manually-wound movement made up of 212 parts, crafted and decorated by hand, opens up whole new vistas in the Reverso legend. In addition to the hours, minutes and small seconds at 6 o'clock, it integrates indications of the 45-hour power-reserve, the moon phases and the diurnal phases. These functions give the Reverso Sun Moon a celestial beauty that confers a truly universal dimension on this unique watch. Its silvered white or black dial welcomes this moon configuration in style. And, suddenly, the Reverso Sun Moon rotates swiftly and smoothly to unveil the other side of its universe, where a transparent crystal reveals the beauty of its apparently weightless movement defying the effects of gravity. A genuine star of high-performance and elegance is born, one which is bound to delight connoisseurs fascinated by the sparkling world of haute horlogerie.

Model available
on white gold bracelet.
275 31 70 (M)
Calibre 823.

Reverso Sun Moon.
18-carat white gold.
Crocodile strap
with white gold
folding buckle.

275 34 70 (M)
Calibre 823.

Model available
on pink gold bracelet.
275 21 20 (M)
Calibre 823.

Reverso Sun Moon.
18-carat pink gold.
Crocodile strap
with pink gold
folding buckle.

275 24 20 (M)
Calibre 823.

"Originally, the only special function the Reverso Sun Moon was to have was the power-reserve", confides Jean-Claude Meylan, who is in charge of developing new movements. But a taste for aesthetic elegance and useful complications led the master-watchmakers of the Manufacture to equip the watch with a moon-phase display. This additional function raised an unexpected difficulty. This is because any moon-phase mechanism goes through a period of two to three hours during which it is impossible to adjust the function. During the assembly phase, this period is generally wedged after midnight. But the Reverso Sun Moon had not scheduled this pause: "At the approval stage for the moon-phase mechanism, we realised that Calibre 823, which had no date, could therefore not show whether the correction jump took place at noon or midnight. We thus had to add a day/night display to distinguish them." It is up to the user to adjust the moon phase at any time of the day... or night.

Jean-Claude Meylan / Head of development

The great day
is finally here

Reverso Date

With its generously-sized day window and a date indication which overlays the conventional time display, Reverso Date immediately asserts its exceptional personality.

Launched in 1933, the "Calendrier" displays the date and day of the week. The round steel case houses LeCoultre Calibre 412.

A day in the life of a master-craftsman: Jaeger-LeCoultre Calibre 836 and its highly innovative day disc, neatly fitted into the upper left-hand corner of the rectangular Reverso Date.

Since 1931, the Reverso has been a landmark in watchmaking history. It proves this once again with the Reverso Date: the hour, minute and small seconds functions are complemented by date and day indications, lending a resolutely innovative look to reading off the time.

While a hand matter-of-factly points its red arrow to the date display, the days of the weeks run past a large off-centre aperture in the upper left segment of the dial. Integrating such a large day disc in this position is a significant feat in itself, made possible by Jaeger-LeCoultre Calibre 836, a mechanical manually-wound movement housed in a steel or 18-carat gold case.

Moreover, driven by a new-found desire to keep time with the motion of the heavens, it now takes on a new dimension in the measurement of time: the version fitted with Calibre 835 features a day/night indication. Through an aperture at 6 o'clock, the small seconds shares its window with that of the sun and stars, a technical performance highlighted by the aesthetic contrast of the black dial with white floral numerals. Clad in 18-carat white gold, the Reverso Date brings time and celestial bodies together under the same canopy of space.

Model available
on white gold bracelet.
274 31 7A/F/D (M)
Calibre 835.

Reverso Date.
18-carat white gold.
Crocodile strap
with white gold
folding buckle.

274 34 7A/F/D (M)
Calibre 835.

Model available
on ostrich strap
with folding buckle.
273 84 2A/F/D (M)
Calibre 836.

Reverso Date.
Stainless steel.

273 81 2A/F/D (M)
Calibre 836.

Model available
on pink gold bracelet.
273 21 2A/F/D (M)
Calibre 836.

Reverso Date.
18-carat pink gold.
Crocodile strap
with pink gold
folding buckle.

273 24 2A/F/D (M)
Calibre 836.

Reverso Duo

The second dial is fitted with a 24-hour indication, enabling one to check the time around the globe, wherever one may be.

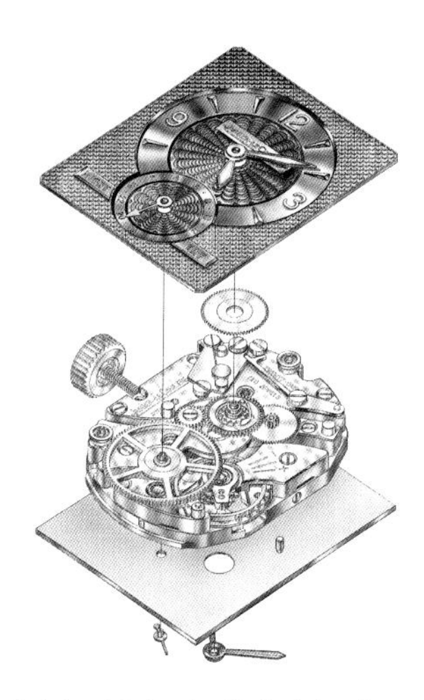

Two dials back to back, with their hands turning in opposite directions: Calibre 854 is a genius of duality at the heart of a single watch. Just one movement gives life to the two faces of the Reverso Duo.

Much of the Reverso's charm lies in its ability to surprise. For more than 70 years, it has been turning its back on time to reveal a personalized engraving, the magic of its mechanism, or simply the radiance of gold or polished steel.

The Reverso Duo actually shows two faces of time. On the front, the time you are currently experiencing; and on the back, the time in the time-zone of your choice, complete with 24-hour indication, so that you can keep constant track of time from one side of the globe to the other. The genius of this timekeeper lies in its two different dials with separately adjusted functions. The two pairs of hands, turning in opposite directions, are nonetheless driven by a single mechanical manually-wound movement. Calibre 854 is a masterpiece of complexity and precision, incorporating a tiny clutch to disengage the hands from the movement when setting the second time-zone. And to allow you to follow the movement of celestial bodies at all times, Jaeger-LeCoultre has created a second version of the Reverso Duo, enriched thanks to Calibre 854J with a new feature: its first time-zone, the one that shows the time here and now, has a day/night indicator. The ingenuity and art of the master-watchmakers at the Manufacture combine to give you the rare pleasure of owning two watches in one.

Model available
on white gold bracelet.
272 31 40 (M)
Calibre 854J.

Reverso Duo.
18-carat white gold.
Crocodile strap
with white gold
folding buckle.

272 34 40 (M)
Calibre 854J.

Model available
on yellow gold bracelet.
271 11 20 (M)
Calibre 854.

Reverso Duo.
18-carat yellow gold.
Crocodile strap
with yellow gold
folding buckle.

271 14 20 (M)
Calibre 854.

Model available
on stainless steel bracelet.
271 81 70 (M)
Calibre 854.

Reverso Duo.
Stainless steel.
Ostrich strap
with folding buckle.

271 84 70 (M)
Calibre 854.

This tiny clutch disengages the movement from the under-dial work when setting the second time-zone.

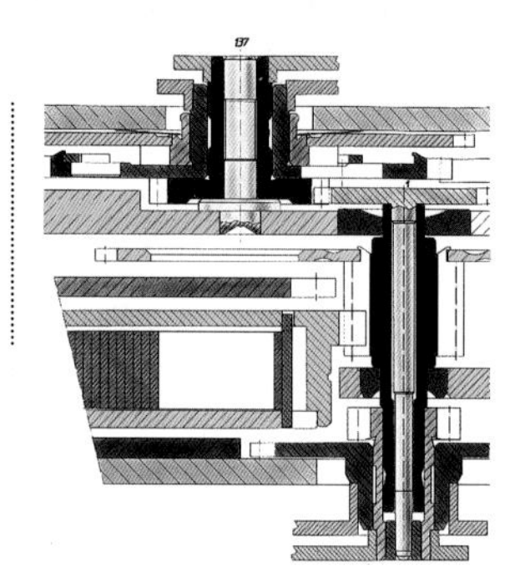

How could one use a single movement to make the hands on two opposite-facing dials turn in the right direction? Design-engineer Roger Guignard recalls the challenge of the Reverso Duo: "The main trick was the connection that goes through the centre of the movement and meshes with the cannon-pinion on the other side." A delicate fine-tuning process for this masterpiece of complexity with its twin faces.

Roger Guignard / Design-engineer

Model available on pink gold bracelet.
271 21 70 (M)
Calibre 854.

Reverso Duo.
18-carat pink gold.
Crocodile strap with pink gold folding buckle.

271 24 70 (M)
Calibre 854.

"Worn down by wind, water and the passing years, rock face becomes velvet, and mineral becomes light. Like the hand of time, man becomes one with matter and tames it in order to make it evolve towards other forms of alchemy. Thus, on the borderlines of a dream world, a magical tale is born, in which `once upon a time' becomes a new reality." The artisans of this enchantment are polishers Marco Frau, Benoît Lime and Serge Diot, who fashion each part in the image of perfection.

JAEGER-LECOULTRE

VI

Reverso Classiques

Avant-garde since 1931

Reverso Classiques

"Classique" – the case of the original 1931 Reverso.

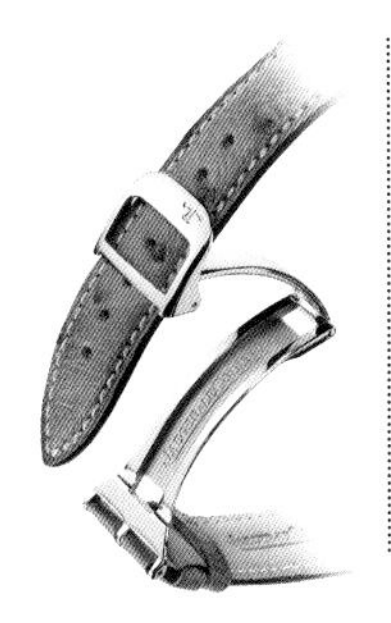

All Reverso watches are fitted with folding buckles (available in three sizes) offering added security when you put your watch on or remove it. It also guarantees a longer life for your leather strap.

Reverso, the legendary swivel watch in the size and style of your choice. Thanks to constant renewal in terms of interpretation and technique, the Reverso has embodied elegance and novelty for more than 70 years.

The creative possibilities afforded by its original concept give rise to the most inventive combinations and the most varied complications. When it was first created in 1931, the Reverso came in a single size only. Today, it has generated a highly diversified line of timekeepers, each endowed with a distinctive personality, yet all imbued with the unique character of the original Reverso. Major investments in research, tools and machinery have enabled the creation of three other sizes: Reverso Grande Taille, Reverso Lady and the tiny Reverso 101, fitted with the world's smallest mechanical movement. Driven by a boundless passion for innovation, the Reverso lends itself to a wide variety of styles which further enhance its uniqueness. For example, a personalised engraving may be made on the case-back and either gem-set or enamelled, according to tastes and wishes. In another mode, by playing on the duality of its front and back, it shows two different faces thanks to the back-to-back dials of the Reverso Duetto: understated elegance by day and sparkling seduction by night. It also asserts its technical refinement through creations merging the watchmaking art with haute joaillerie, such as the Reverso Florale which, through adorning the swirling tendrils on its case with brilliants, becomes a genuine jewel of rare beauty.

More presence – mechanically

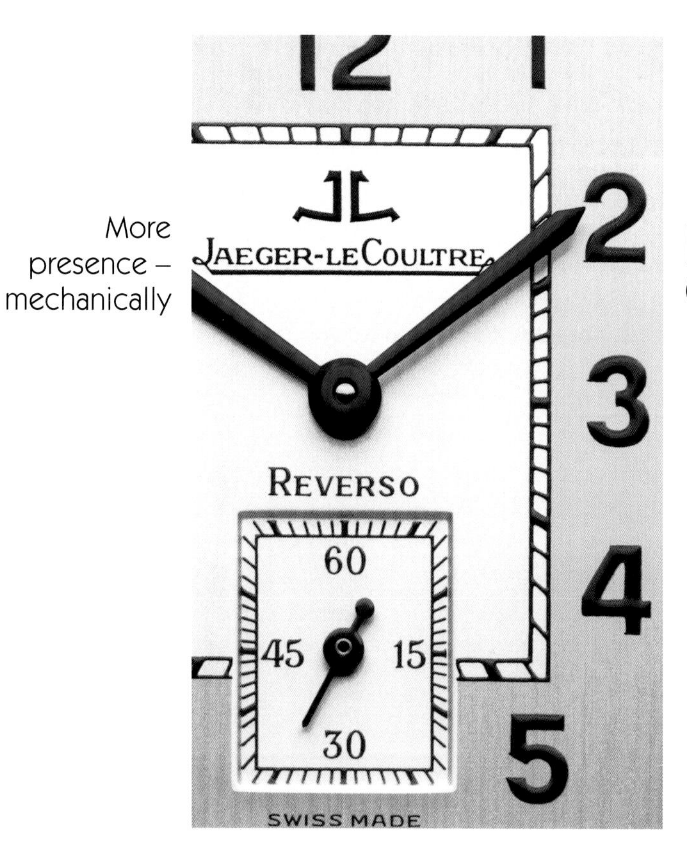

Reverso Grande Taille

First created in 1991, the Reverso Grande Taille houses Jaeger-LeCoultre manually-wound Calibre 822, specially made for this case.

Reverso Grande Taille.
18-carat yellow gold.
Crocodile strap
with yellow gold
folding buckle.

270 14 20 (M)
Calibre 822.

Model available
on ostrich strap
with stainless steel
folding buckle.
270 54 20 (M)
Calibre 822.

Reverso Grande Taille.
18-carat yellow gold.

270 11 20 (M)
Calibre 822.

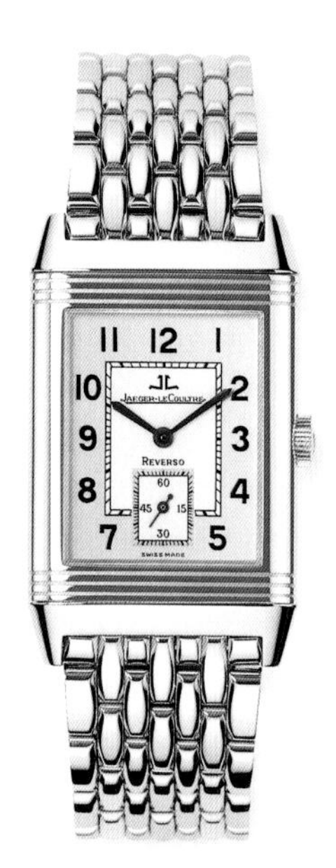

Reverso Grande Taille.
18-carat yellow gold
and stainless steel.

270 51 20 (M)
Calibre 822.

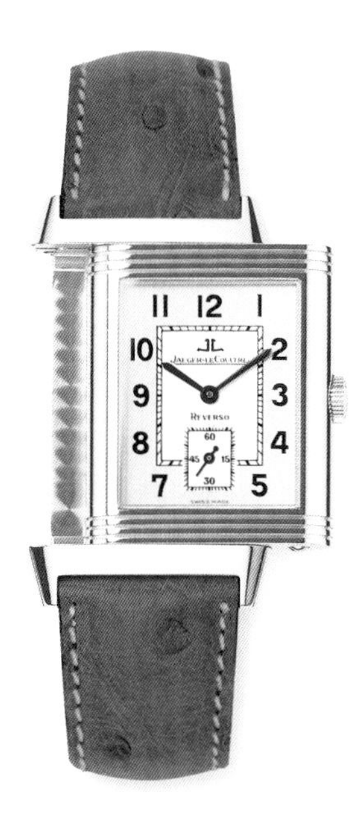

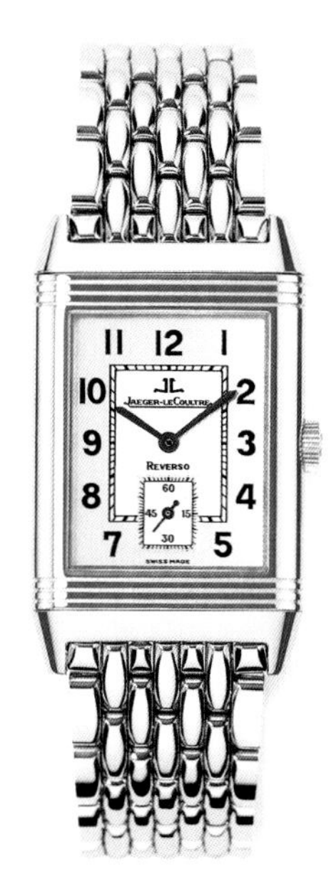

Reverso Grande Taille.
Stainless steel.
Ostrich strap
with folding buckle.

270 84 20 (M)
Calibre 822.

Reverso Grande Taille.
Stainless steel.

270 81 20 (M)
Calibre 822.

The Reverso in
its original version
since 1931

Reverso Classique

The face of the Reverso Classique retains the exact proportions of the 1931 watch, but the body is slightly slimmer. The Manufacture's master-watchmakers created a smaller movement, Calibre 846, to give added refinement to the classic Art Deco look. (This model can be decorated with a lacquered engraving on request).

Model available
on yellow gold and
stainless steel bracelet.
250 51 20 (M)
Calibre 846.
251 51 20 (Q)
Calibre 608.

Reverso Classique.
18-carat yellow gold
and stainless steel.
Ostrich strap
with stainless steel
folding buckle.

250 54 20 (M)
Calibre 846.

251 54 20 (Q)
Calibre 608.

"The more complicated an engraving, the more interest it arouses. The motifs I prefer doing are faces, as each is different from the others, and recreating their expressions calls for the greatest attention. First one traces the outlines of the drawing with a dry-point, which slightly scratches the metal. This makes it possible to wipe out any errors with a buff. Then comes the engraving itself, done with burins or gravers; mistakes at this stage are out of the question! I adopted the same technique in engraving the Reverso Florale Tiaré. Among the most beautiful works one can create are gem-set engravings. The fact of having to "tame" both the metal and the precious stones is a source of great personal satisfaction."

Dominique Vuez / Master-engraver

Model available on ostrich strap with yellow gold folding buckle.
250 14 20 (M)
Calibre 846.
251 14 20 (Q)
Calibre 608.

Reverso Classique.
18-carat yellow gold.

250 11 20 (M)
Calibre 846.

251 11 20 (Q)
Calibre 608.

Reverso Classique.
Stainless steel.
Ostrich strap
with folding buckle.

250 84 20 (M)
Calibre 846.

251 84 20 (Q)
Calibre 608.

Reverso Classique.
Stainless steel.

250 81 20 (M)
Calibre 846.

251 81 20 (Q)
Calibre 608.

The avant-garde
from a feminine
perspective

Reverso Lady

Jaeger-LeCoultre has dedicated the Reverso Lady quite simply to women. The personalised engraving on the case-back makes this tribute yet more unique: a monogram, significant date, sign of the zodiac, coat-of-arms or any other symbol of particular importance will create an even more intimate link between the Reverso and the lady who wears it.

Reverso Lady.
18-carat yellow gold.
Crocodile strap
with yellow gold
folding buckle.

260 14 20 (M)
Calibre 846.

261 14 20 (Q)
Calibre 608.

Model available
on ostrich strap
with stainless steel
folding buckle.
260 54 20 (M)
Calibre 846.
261 54 20 (Q)
Calibre 608.

Reverso Lady.
18-carat yellow gold.

260 11 20 (M)
Calibre 846.

261 11 20 (Q)
Calibre 608.

Reverso Lady.
18-carat yellow gold
and stainless steel.

260 51 20 (M)
Calibre 846.

261 51 20 (Q)
Calibre 608.

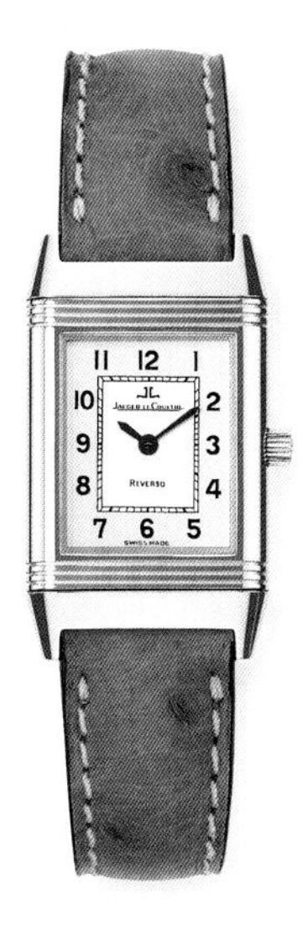

Reverso Lady.
Stainless steel.
Ostrich strap
with folding buckle.

260 84 20 (M)
Calibre 846.

261 84 20 (Q)
Calibre 608.

Reverso Lady.
Stainless steel.

260 81 20 (M)
Calibre 846.

261 81 20 (Q)
Calibre 608.

Reverso Florale

Setting the entire circumference of the reversible case with diamonds was a daunting challenge in creating the Reverso Florale. To achieve this feat, the level of precision in gem-setting had to be extremely high, and even more so, because watchmakers had chosen to confront the hardness of steel.

Reverso Florale models may be engraved with specially-created Belle Epoque initials or with the motif or message of your choice. Engraving on models in gold or steel and gold may be set with precious stones.

Sixty-four VVSI Top Wesselton full-cut diamonds enhance the icy beauty of steel, one of the hardest metals to set with precious stones. The exceptional technical prowess of the Jaeger-LeCoultre master-jewellers is seen here to perfection.

A tribute to contemporary Woman? Who better than the Reverso Florale to undertake such a delicate mission! Engravers and gemsetters combine their talents to make this timekeeper into a gem of natural beauty.

The hardness of the metal provides a perfect foil for the sparkling diamonds, expressing the most elegant of compliments to the wearer. The brilliance of this model is, noblesse oblige, gracefully underlined by the new Belle Epoque lettering which may be custom engraved on the case-back. Reverso Florale houses quartz Calibre 608, decorated by hand. In gold, gold and steel or steel versions, extended by a leather strap or an exclusive 5-link bracelet, it is driven by just one desire: to fire the imagination of women who long to recapture the charm of a bygone era.

Whether engraved or gem-set, the new Belle Epoque lettering brings a very personal touch to the Reverso Florale.

Model available
on crocodile strap
with yellow gold
folding buckle.
265 14 20 (Q)
Calibre 608.

Reverso Florale.
18-carat yellow gold
set with diamonds.
Yellow gold bracelet.

265 11 20 (Q)
Calibre 608.

Reverso Florale.
18-carat yellow gold and stainless steel set with diamonds.
Crocodile strap with stainless steel folding buckle.

265 54 20 (Q)
Calibre 608.

Reverso Florale.
18-carat yellow gold and stainless steel set with diamonds.
Yellow gold and stainless steel bracelet.

265 51 20 (Q)
Calibre 608.

Reverso Florale.
Stainless steel
set with diamonds.
Crocodile strap
with folding buckle.

265 84 20 (Q)
Calibre 608.

Reverso Florale.
Stainless steel
set with diamonds.
Stainless steel bracelet.

265 81 20 (Q)
Calibre 608.

"From the infinitesimal to the boundless horizon and from the immensity surrounding us to the infinitely precise. This to-and-fro movement of the mind, a wellspring of creative inspiration, is an essential resource in the art of engraving. Projecting one's gaze to faraway places in order to be infused by the wonders of the world, before reducing them to a microcosmic scale, and then retracing reality right down to the smallest details." By allowing his gaze to wander, Dominique Vuez captures the very essence of the beauty reflected in his engravings.

Elegance
around the clock –
the graceful ballet
of night and day

Reverso Duetto

On the back, sophistication and
refined elegance: a sparkling interpretation
of the truly exceptional.

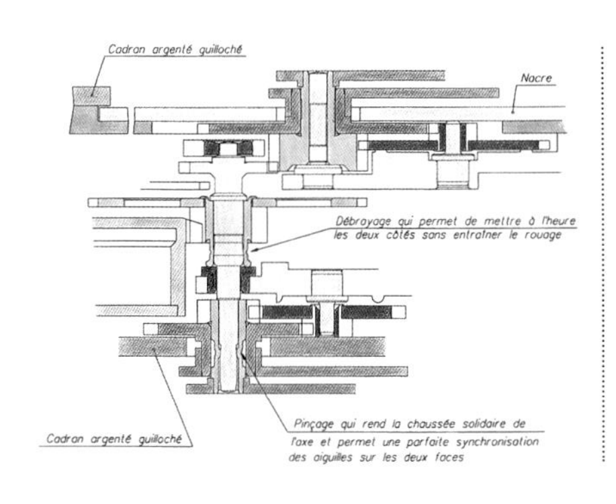

The main difficulty for the Reverso Duetto and its tiny movement was to create a perfect symbiosis between its two dials. Design-engineer Rachel Torresani tells of the whims and fancies of this watch which seeks to lend beauty to the rhythm of your days and nights: "One could not allow for even the slightest discrepancy. The cannon-pinion had to turn in accordance with the central arbor, in order to transmit the movement to the other side without any play. However, because they were so small, the parts raised considerable indenting problems: they split or ovalised when held with pliers and tended to seize up. It took six long months to find solutions, remake the prototypes several times and finally stabilise the indenting."

Rachel Torresani / Design-engineer

To be or not to be a woman? For the Reverso Duetto, that is simply not an issue: it is every inch a woman. Day-side or night-side, it remains beautiful or elegant in all circumstances. Its dual nature makes it a watch unique in its kind. Two back-to-back dials, two pairs of hands driven by the same movement, turning in opposite directions: the ingenious charm of this twin-faced watch is a real head-turner. And as if to double its fascinating assets, Jaeger-LeCoultre has created the Reverso Duetto in two different sizes.

Originally crafted in the ladies size, it houses Jaeger-LeCoultre Calibre 844, one of the world's smallest manually-wound movements with double hand-fitting. On the front, its guilloché dial with floral numerals exudes an understated appeal that accompanies you throughout the day. On the back, the silvered mother-of-pearl dial is enhanced by the sparkle of its brilliants. It thereby perfectly reflects the symbiosis between fine jewellery and prestige watchmaking. The Reverso Duetto classic size follows closely in its footsteps. In this more generous dimension, it beats to the rhythm of patented Calibre 865, a mechanical manually-wound movement. The front is endowed with a small seconds function and the silvered guilloché dial features blued steel fan-shaped hands flitting over floral numerals, while the back is illuminated by the 32 diamonds framing the bezel. Exclusively feminine, the Reverso Duetto mirrors a vision of time dedicated to beauty, elegance and sensitivity, along with a passion for mechanical watchmaking.

Reverso Duetto.
Stainless steel
set with diamonds.
Crocodile strap
with folding buckle.

266 84 20 (M)
Calibre 844.

Model availale
on yellow gold
and stainless
steel bracelet.
266 51 20 (M)
Calibre 844.

Reverso Duetto.
Stainless steel
set with diamonds.
Stainless steel
bracelet.

266 81 20 (M)
Calibre 844.

Reverso Duetto.
18-carat yellow gold
and stainless steel
set with diamonds.
Crocodile strap with stainless
steel folding buckle.

266 54 20 (M)
Calibre 844.

Reverso Duetto.
18-carat yellow gold
set with diamonds.
Crocodile strap
with yellow gold
folding buckle.

266 14 20 (M)
Calibre 844.

Reverso Duetto.
18-carat yellow gold
set with diamonds.
Yellow gold bracelet.

266 11 20 (M)
Calibre 844.

"Gentle yet powerful, water surges its way into the earth to find imperturbable rest. Its outlines fit so seamlessly into its environment that one could almost believe it has been in this very same place since the dawn of time. This perfection of matter sculpted by nature is a supreme model for the finish on the parts assembled within our watches." Paul Faure-Comte, Chantal Lelandais and Jocelyne Horvath devote the same skill to trimming the noble metal components and thus preparing them to take up their assigned place in the overall scheme of things.

Reverso Duetto Classique

Synchronizing the day and night watch faces is no mere dream. It is the role of Jaeger-LeCoultre patented Calibre 865, which beats at the heart of the Classique size case of the Reverso Duetto.

Model available
on white
gold bracelet.
256 31 70 (M)
Calibre 865.

Reverso Duetto.
18-carat white gold
set with diamonds.
Crocodile strap
with white gold
folding buckle.

256 34 70 (M)
Calibre 865.

Reverso Duetto.
18-carat yellow gold
set with diamonds.
Crocodile strap with
yellow gold
folding buckle.

256 14 20 (M)
Calibre 865.

Reverso Duetto.
18-carat yellow gold
set with diamonds.
Yellow gold bracelet.

256 11 20 (M)
Calibre 865.

Reverso Duetto.
Stainless steel set
with diamonds.
Crocodile strap
with folding buckle.

256 84 20 (M)
Calibre 865.

Reverso Duetto.
Stainless steel set
with diamonds.
Stainless steel bracelet.

256 81 20 (M)
Calibre 865.

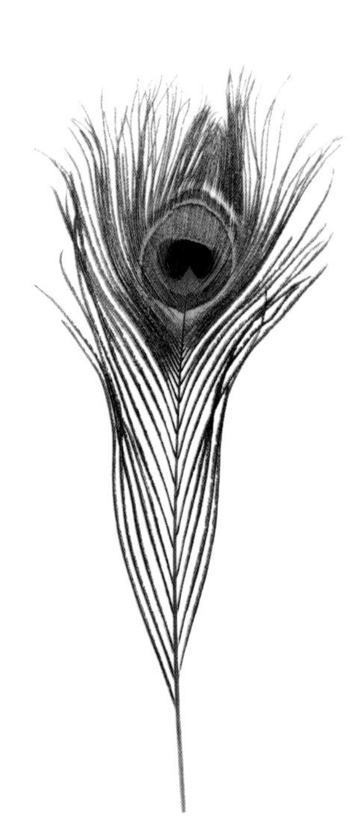

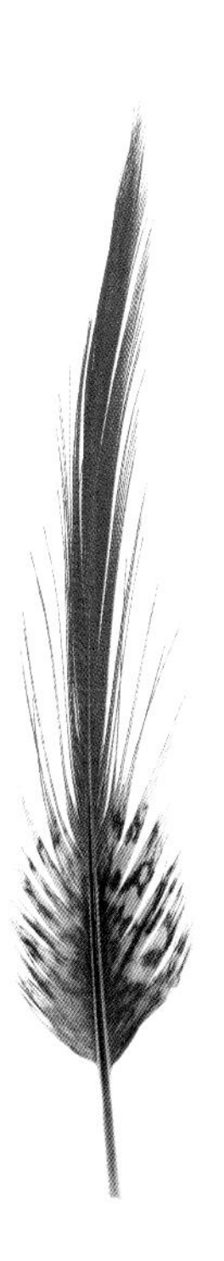

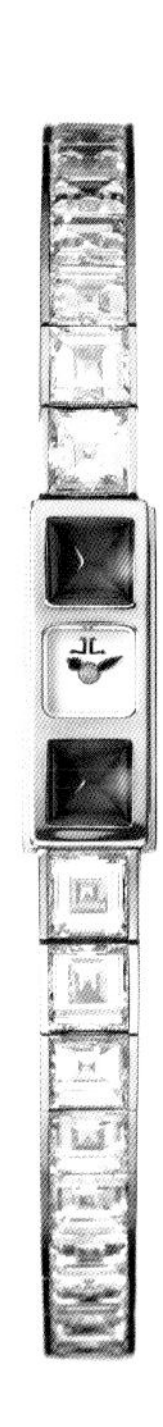

VII

Joaillerie

Les folies horlogères

124

Watchmaking refinement at its most precious

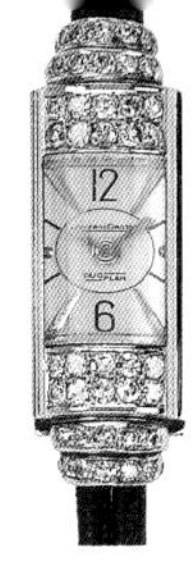

A 1927 Duoplan brilliantly displays the creative possibilities of miniature watchmaking and precious stones in an Art Deco setting.

Every age reveals its character in fancy watchmaking. This ring in white gold fitted with a Calibre 426 movement dates from 1941.

The world's tiniest mechanical watch movement caught the eye of the world's grandest monarch, Queen Elizabeth II, who wore the Jaeger-LeCoultre Calibre 101 on her coronation day.

A tiny wristwatch with a big story to tell. Since wristwatches became popular in the 1920s, designers have always sought to let time escape the parameters of a conventional watch so that it could adorn a lady's wrist. Feminine individuality is always a welcome inspiration for Jaeger-LeCoultre's stylists, as they stretch technical limits to accommodate whims of shape and size.

In 1925, the Manufacture developed a watch movement that opened the way for the tiny, diamond-paved rectangular watches so necessary in the Jazz Age. The Calibre 104 movement, constructed on two levels, made possible an Art Deco watch measuring just 19.8 mm long by 8.4 mm wide. Inspired by the diamond-set Duoplan's success, the Manufacture's watchmakers went even further in miniaturization. In 1929 they created the extraordinary Calibre 101, which has remained the world's smallest mechanical movement to this day. The skeletonized version, which weighs less than a gram, is certainly also the world's lightest watch movement. The tiny Calibres 426 (1941) and 430 (1968), with concealed crowns, made a variety of specialities possible – including a jewelled ring-watch. Today, Jaeger-LeCoultre makes a lady's fancy come true in the special Reverso jewellery models. Giving the world's smallest mechanical movement the dimension of a prodigious jewel... Jaeger-LeCoultre continues to push back the limits of what is technically possible, entering a universe of endless dreams. Crowning the Reverso 101 with

The Reverso Duetto in 18-carat yellow gold provides a precious home for the horological refinement of Jaeger-LeCoultre Calibre 844. The sparkle of diamonds emphasises the duality of this incomparable jewellery-watch.

The Reverso Montre de poche "Emeraude" is a vibrant expression of the gem-setting art. 836 round diamonds, 69 baguette-cut diamonds and 160 emeralds envelop the swivel case of this watchmaking wonder. Its guilloché mother of-pearl dial displays the time along with small seconds, thermometer and power-reserve.

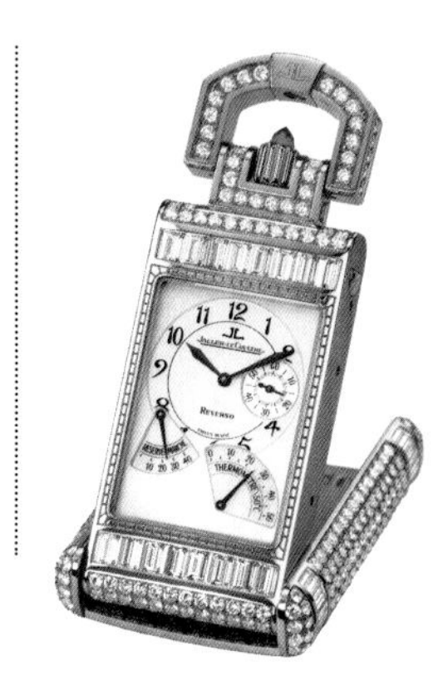

marvellous gems; adorning Calibre 844 of the Reverso Duetto with matchless refinement; or enriching the artistic appeal of the Reverso Montre de poche with a power-reserve movement, small seconds hand and integrated thermometer: all the facets of the watchmaking art shine through such feats. Designers, gem-setters and master-watchmakers unite their talents to excel in the art of the jewellery watch. For not only do these pieces of jewellery house the most varied complications known to timekeepers, they are also masterpieces demonstrating a wealth of creativity. A legend with a myriad faces, the Reverso demands tremendous precision and more than exceptional mastery from those who seek to set these unique watches with gems. Whether adorned with 32 coloured stones or pavé with more than 3,000 brilliants, the perfect mobility of its swivelling case is never lost sight of: nothing must disturb the "turn of the century". Offering avant-garde performance and the most prodigious jewellery folies of all time: Jaeger-LeCoultre has plenty of surprises in store for aficionados of fine watchmaking who love to be dazzled by the sparkle of its haute joaillerie creations.

"Let's cultivate our mind as we cultivate our garden," wrote Voltaire. "Drawing nourishment from the principles governing our sphere of life and inspiration from the nuances outlining the hills and valleys of our perception. Allowing our thoughts to gather nectar and pollen freely before returning to water our creative furrows with fresh ideas that can bloom in tune with time." It is by drawing upon their deepest inner resources that designers Janek Deleskiewicz, Magali Métrailler and Sam Wühl lovingly cultivate the garden of Jaeger-LeCoultre.

Not too small
to be a genuine
Reverso

Reverso 101

Much like its minute calibre,
the case of the Reverso 101
takes the legendary swivel watch
to extremes in miniaturisation.

The Reverso 101 combines two of this century's watchmaking breakthroughs - the swivel case and the smallest mechanical movement ever made. The case, which turns through 360°, has a volume of only 1.5 cc. Yet it consists of 41 separate parts and houses the 98 parts of a movement weighing approximately one gram.

When watchmaking
miniaturization
marries haute joaillerie,
the Manufacture
Jaeger-LeCoultre is more
than happy
to exchange rings!

In its jewellery version, the Reverso 101 reaches a new peak of perfection. How else could one define the perfect alignment of around 4,000 gems, totalling around 10 carats of top-quality diamonds, all ideally cut and set? The Calibre 101 developed by Jaeger-LeCoultre in 1929 is entered in the Guinness Book of Records as the smallest mechanical watch movement in the world. Only two watch-makers in the Manufacture today know the trick of assembling the 98 different parts into a fully functioning movement that measures just 14 x 4.8 x 3.4 mm. It is a job that takes them a whole week to complete. The Calibre 101, also known as the "2 lignes", is a rectangular movement especially conceived for elongated watches. Among the creations made possible by this tiny mechanism is the diamond-set watch Queen Elizabeth II wore at her coronation.

Other models
available
on request.

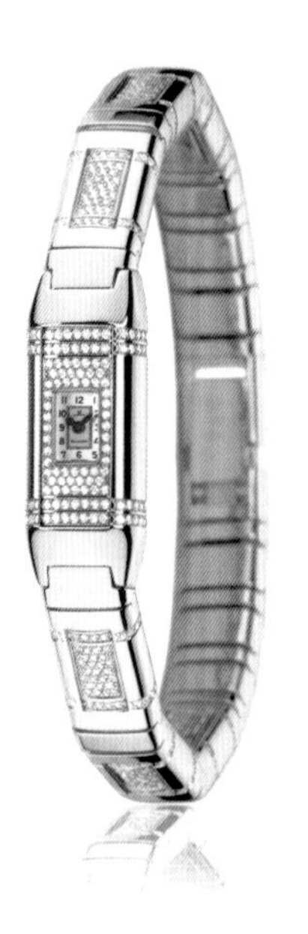

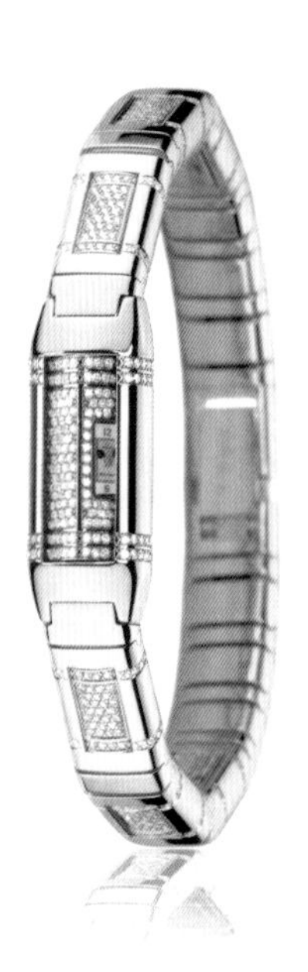

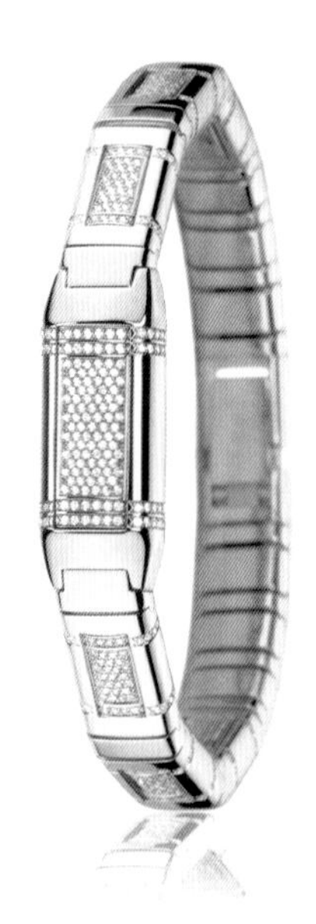

Reverso 101.
18-carat yellow gold
set with diamonds.
Yellow gold bracelet
set with diamonds.

280 12 01 (M)
Calibre 101.

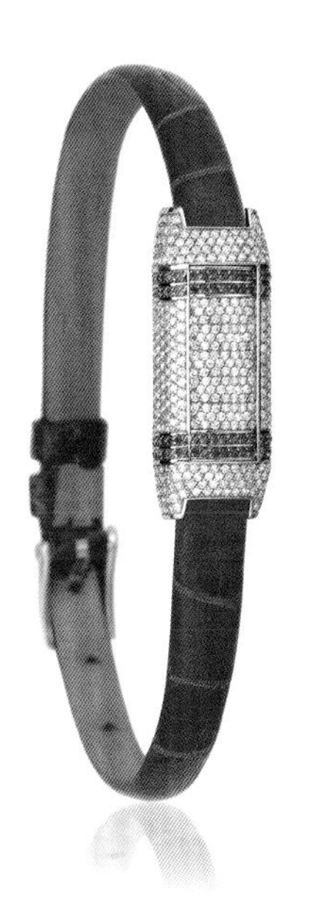

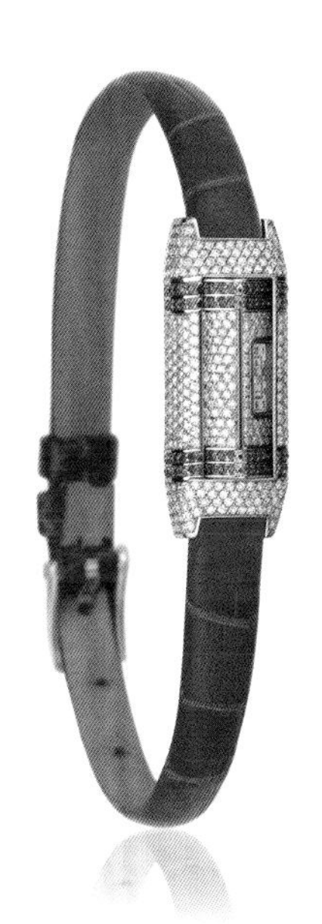

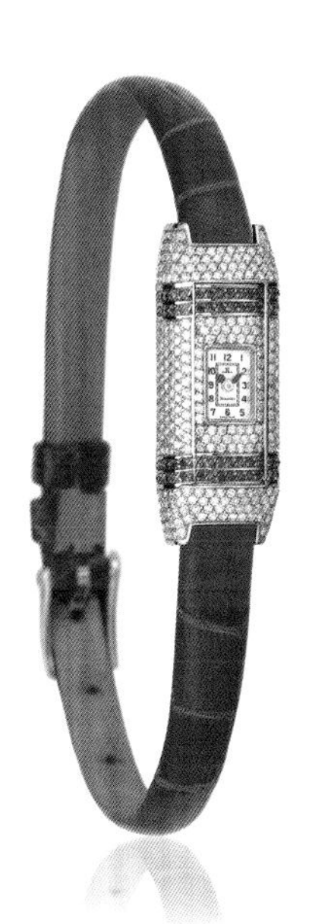

Reverso 101.
18-carat white gold set with diamonds and rubies. Crocodile strap with white gold buckle set with diamonds.

280 35 01 (M)
Calibre 101.

A river of diamonds for the world's smallest movement

Joaillerie Rivière 101

The Joaillerie Rivière 101 clothes its diminutive movement in dazzling light. A river of diamonds for a miniature watchmaking marvel.

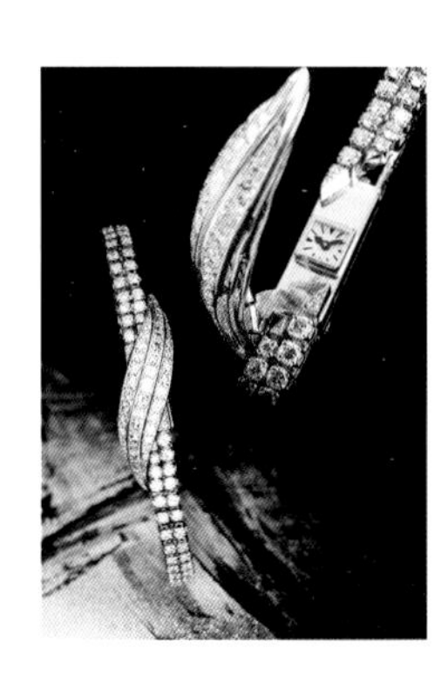

The ladies "2 lignes" watch was so named because of the size of its movement, Calibre 101, was formerly measured in "lignes". In 1959, the world's smallest mechanical movement was splendidly encased within a diamond-set piece of jewellery featuring an entirely pavé cover and a bracelet set with two rows of diamonds.

Travelling back in time, while charting unexplored horizons in watchmaking creativity and sailing through changing tastes in a peerlessly exceptional and daring manner… Such is the challenge encapsulated for Jaeger-LeCoultre by the Joaillerie Rivière 101.

An exquisite haute joaillerie creation, it literally radiates Jaeger-LeCoultre's vision of watchmaking and women, in a model celebrating feminine grace and the art of horology. This aesthetic treasure houses the minute rectangular Calibre 101, the famous tiny movement created to beat at the heart of the smallest gems crafted by the Manufacture. And although it is the world's smallest mechanical movement, its power-reserve provides around 33 hours of autonomy. The Joaillerie Rivière 101 is clad in the gleaming beauty of white gold. On the case, two diamonds as large as Calibre 101 itself frame the dial as if to echo the prodigious movement concealed within. The silvered dial is distinguished by the delicacy of its slender leaf-type hands.

This timekeeper comes in three different variations which underscore its rarity and the technical accomplishment it embodies. The first represents the ultimate in understated elegance. Its bracelet is made up of 32 square bevelled links, mirror-polished to shine like a constellation of stars. The second is set with 140 diamonds, surrounding its precious mechanism like a translucent halo. Finally, representing the crowning glory, the Joaillerie Rivière 101 glows like a river of light, each of its 41 links set with a square diamond.

Model available on a
white gold bracelet on
which each of the 32 links
is set with 4 diamonds.
281 33 02 (M)
Calibre 101.

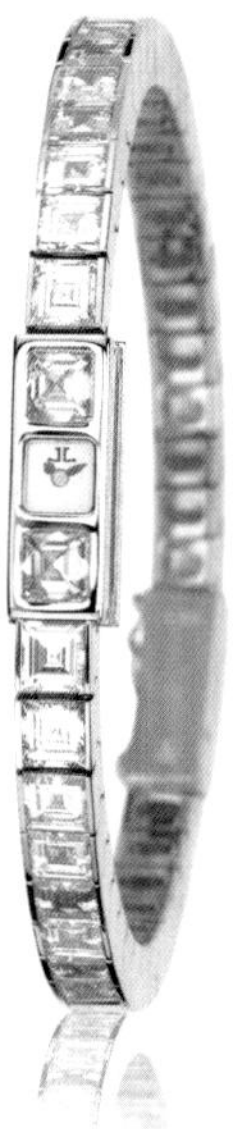

Joaillerie Rivière 101.
18-carat white gold
set with diamonds.
White gold bracelet
set with diamonds.

281 33 01 (M)
Calibre 101.

Joaillerie Rivière 101.
18-carat white gold
set with diamonds.
White gold bracelet.

281 31 01 (M)
Calibre 101.

"Nature leaves nothing to chance. A ray of light, the veins in a leaf: each detail is placed exactly where it should be, making up a living puzzle that vibrates to the rhythm of the seasons. Gem-setting a time-keeper implies recreating the authenticity of this magic with its multiple facets, playing on the space, thickness and surface of the matter, on its shadows and its shimmering." Jewellers Alain Kirchof, Eric Frey and Christophe Golay make each Jaeger-LeCoultre into a fairytale miniature landscape.

A watchmaking gem blossoms

Reverso Florale Tiaré

The Reverso Florale Tiaré represents the blossoming of numerous artistic talents. For each watch, the engravers, gem-setters and designers select 168 diamonds to adorn the engraved floral motif.

The gem-set engraving on the Reverso Florale Tiaré calls for meticulous work performed in several stages. First, the three flowers are drawn on tracing paper, placed on the unfolded case. Each flower is then individually set with gems. Engraving constitutes the final touch, fine-tuning the outlines and leaving no margin for the slightest error.

Like a botanical muse, the tiaré flower served to inspire the theme of the Reverso Florale. Won over by its natural charms, Jaeger-LeCoultre's jeweller-gemmologist Sam Wühl chose it from among the multitude of flowers colouring our world.

To create the Reverso Florale Tiaré, designers, engravers and gem-setters focused their talents around the legendary swivel case in 18-carat gold, set with 64 diamonds. They clad the available surface with flowers of different shapes, then selected precious stones to adorn the engraved motif. The final delicate touch was given by the engraver's dexterity: perfectly rounding the shapes to give each flower an enchantingly soft outline. Three delightful tiaré flowers thus follow on from each other in a single motif, wrapping the case in their delicate tendrils... The 104 diamonds carefully selected for each watch underscore the radiance of this enchanting vision: from the petals to the triangular hearts, they make the rim of the case shine like a corolla. In this manner, each timekeeper is transformed into a unique gem of femininity. This subtle blend of understatement and technical refinement conveys innate grace and sophistication, breathing in time with Calibre 608. The floral numerals on the front play with the shimmering mother-of-pearl at the centre of the silvered dial. Simple and precious, elegant and mischievous, the Reverso Florale Tiaré represents the blossoming of an artistic gem which Jaeger-LeCoultre dedicates to women with a taste for fine watchmaking.

Reverso Florale Tiaré.
18-carat yellow gold
set with diamonds.
Flower pattern.
Yellow gold bracelet.

265 11 01 (Q)
Calibre 608.

Reverso Florale Tiaré.
18-carat yellow gold
set with diamonds.
Flower pattern.
Crocodile strap with yellow
gold folding buckle.

265 14 01 (Q)
Calibre 608.

Queen of the islands, the tiaré flower inspired the theme of the Reverso Florale: "Won over by its natural charms and its language of love, we chose it to adorn the Reverso case. We were looking for a timeless flower that would give free rein to individual imagination. We therefore redesigned the tiaré flower as an "illustration," complementing its feminine gentleness with a playful side that is an invitation to dreams and to mysticism. In order to entirely clothe the Reverso, we worked on the unfolded case placed flat, like a comic book. This technique enabled us to achieve a continuous, uninterrupted motif all around the case. After being set with gems, the three tiaré flowers are meticulously engraved to perfect their rounded forms which delicately wreathe their way around the case."

Sam Wühl / Jeweller-gemmologist

Elegance around
the clock –
the graceful ballet
of night and day

Reverso Duetto

On the back, the Reverso Duetto radiates a luminous glow: its dial enhanced by brilliants underlines its taste for sophistication.

Jaeger-LeCoultre Calibre 844 housed in the Reverso Duetto and its double hand-fitting: or how to make the two hands on the front turn one way and the two hands on the back turn the other way.

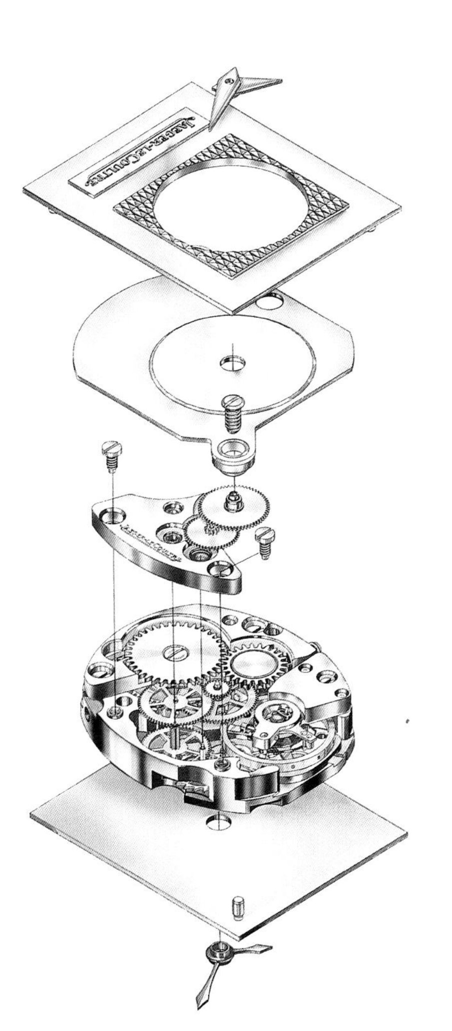

Reverso Duetto expresses brilliant duality within just one timekeeper; the power of a watchmaking passion that beats steadily at the heart of precious aesthetic refinement, blending sheer elegance and exceptional jewellery creativity.

The front side exudes a subtle form of seduction, with the elegance of its case discreetly emphasised by the diamonds set on the lugs and sides. The silvered dial with its floral numerals reflects a natural charm that becomes the finest daily statement of personality. The sophistication of the back glitters with the sparkle of diamonds gently caressing the silvered gem-set mother-of-pearl dial. Both entrancing worlds are driven by a single mechanical manually-wound movement with double hand-fitting: Jaeger-LeCoultre Calibre 844, one of the smallest in the world. In creating the Reverso Duetto, Jaeger-LeCoultre sought to achieve a perfect symbiosis of the watchmaking art and haute joaillerie. Mission accomplished.

Reverso Duetto.
18-carat white gold
set with diamonds.
White gold bracelet
set with diamonds.

266 33 01 (M)
Calibre 844.

Model available
on all-metal white
gold bracelet.
266 31 01 (M)
Calibre 844.

Reverso Duetto.
18-carat white gold
set with diamonds.
White gold bracelet
set with diamonds.

266 32 01 (M)
Calibre 844.

Reverso Duetto.
18-carat white gold
set with diamonds.
Crocodile strap with white
gold folding buckle.

266 34 01 (M)
Calibre 844.

Reverso Duetto.
18-carat yellow gold
set with diamonds.
Yellow gold bracelet
set with diamonds.

266 13 01 (M)
Calibre 844.

Reverso Duetto.
18-carat yellow gold
set with diamonds.
Yellow gold bracelet
set with diamonds.

266 12 01 (M)
Calibre 844.

Reverso Duetto.
18-carat yellow gold
set with diamonds.
Yellow gold bracelet.

266 11 01 (M)
Calibre 844.

Reverso Duetto.
18-carat yellow gold
set with diamonds.
Crocodile strap with yellow
gold folding buckle.

266 14 01 (M)
Calibre 844.

The Reverso
turns on the colours
of the moment

Reverso Joaillerie 3 cabochons

Three blue sapphire cabochons, oval-cut for the case and round for the crown, provide a perfect foil for the fire of the 116 diamonds, lovingly set with virtuoso talent.

The elegance of this
Reverso Joaillerie 3 cabochons
in white gold is signed on the back
by a monogram in "Anglaise"
lettering, set with brilliants.

The legendary swivel watch by Jaeger-LeCoultre turns towards colours and sparkles its way along the chromatic scale. The ability to be flattering, appealing, brilliant yet discreet... such are the talents that the master-watchmakers, designers and gem-setters have lavished upon the Reverso Joaillerie 3 cabochons.

Compelling feminine, it radiates the values of haute horlogerie. This lovely lady combines the irresistible jewellery passion of her 116 diamonds with an unmistakable touch of coquetry: three pastel-blue, pink or yellow sapphires, oval-cut for the case and round for the crown. Nestling at the heart of the floral numerals reminiscent of the Belle Epoque, the mother-of-pearl of the dial, one of the most ancient materials used in jewellery, adds a nostalgic note, as if to remind one that this daringly radiant piece of jewellery is a creation in the noblest watchmaking tradition. This delightful masterpiece is driven by a mechanical manually-wound movement, Jaeger-LeCoultre Calibre 846. Precious and sensible, the Reverso Joaillerie 3 cabochons cultivates its extravagant tastes in harmony with the rules of the watchmaking art and aesthetic codes of elegance. Thus, having chosen straps in pastel-blue, pink or yellow, it opted for white gold in order to harmonise its contrasts. The nobility and understated sheen of this metal provides a timeless backdrop for the elegance of this beauty with her airs of casual grace. And on the other side of the hours and minutes, the back set with 52 diamonds leaves plenty of scope for a personalised engraving.

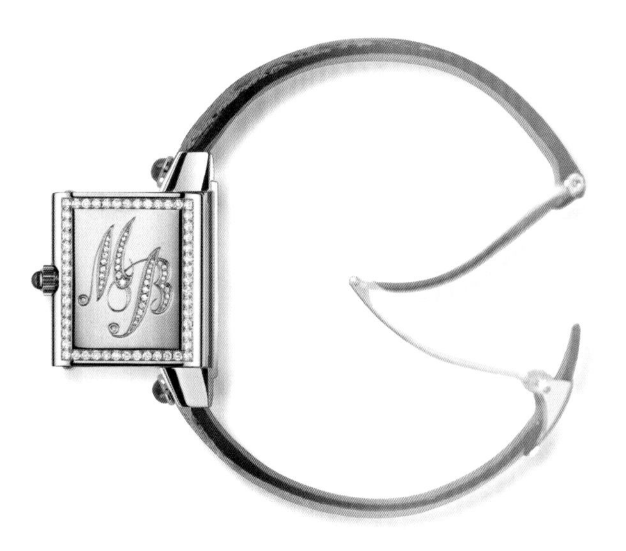

Reverso Joaillerie
3 cabochons.
18-carat white gold
set with diamonds and
3 pastel-blue sapphires.
Crocodile strap with
white gold folding buckle.

262 34 03 (M)
Calibre 846.

Reverso Joaillerie
3 cabochons.
18-carat white gold
set with diamonds and
3 yellow sapphires.
Crocodile strap with
white gold folding buckle.

262 34 01 (M)
Calibre 846.

Reverso Joaillerie
3 cabochons.
18-carat white gold
set with diamonds and
3 pink sapphire cabochons.
Crocodile strap with
white gold folding buckle.

262 34 02 (M)
Calibre 846.

1000 hours
sparkle with
a thousand fires

Master Joaillerie

The Master Grande Memovox underlines the art of watchmaking complication through superlative jewellery refinement. Set with 190 diamonds, this precious pink gold receptacle housing perpetual calendar and alarm mechanisms displays its sophisticated functions on a silvered dial.

Forming an alliance between the rigorous principles of the Master Control 1000 Hours programme and the spectacular creativity of gemmologists; making a reference in technical watchmaking into a jewellery masterpiece.

The Master Ultra-Thin, a masterpiece of miniaturisation, houses the impressive mechanical performance of Calibre 849 within the narrowest possible space. Enhancing its value, this exceptional watch clothes its bezel in 212 diamonds spread over two rows and its crown with 16 diamonds, or dons the most precious of garments by entirely paving its case with 445 diamonds. The major difficulty lies in the extremely slender metal surfaces available, which required the use of the world's smallest diamonds. The other model selected from the range was the Master Grande Memovox, which combines the two most sophisticated useful complications: the perpetual calendar and the alarm function. To accommodate the 349 components of automatic Calibre 909, it has been given a larger case than the other Master models. Representing the expression of watchmaking passion, it welcomes the fanciful charms of haute joaillerie and serves as a precious showcase thanks to its bezel and crown set with 190 diamonds or the entirely pavé rim of its case. This truly masterful piece of work calls for particular care in setting stones of varying dimensions, ranging from 0.7 to 1.7 mm. In this way, two works of art make the Master Control 1000 Hours line shine with a thousand fires.

Model available
with entirely gem-set case.
146 24 02 (A)
Calibre 909.

Master Grande Memovox.
18-carat pink gold
set with diamonds.
Crocodile strap with
pink gold folding buckle.

146 24 01 (A)
Calibre 909.

Master Ultra Thin.
18-carat white gold
set with diamonds.
Crocodile strap with
white gold folding buckle.

145 34 02 (M)
Calibre 849.

Jaeger-LeCoultre accentuates the feat of mechanical miniaturisation represented by the Master Ultra Thin through an unprecedented jewellery feat. "Given the minuscule thickness of its case, it seemed impossible to set the Master Ultra Thin with gems. Determined to prove the contrary, we resorted to the highest technologies within the art of jewellery-making. Especially since, in addition to the extreme finesse of the material available, the Master Ultra Thin implied a second challenge: the miniaturisation of the gemstones themselves. The diamonds selected in their rough state from among the tiniest must be further cut to reach extreme diameters as small as 0.4 mm. The thickness of the stone is virtually the same as that of the metal."

Alain Kirchhof / Jeweller-gemsetter

Model available
with entirely gem-set case.
145 24 02 (M)
Calibre 849.

Master Ultra Thin.
18-carat white gold
set with diamonds.
Crocodile strap with
white gold folding buckle.

145 34 01 (M)
Calibre 849.

Master Ultra Thin.
18-carat pink gold
set with diamonds.
Crocodile strap with
pink gold folding buckle.

145 24 01 (M)
Calibre 849.

"What a superficial glance may find ordinary, becomes extraordinary if observed closer up. The elements of our daily surroundings are a given whose riches are often forgotten. By focusing on a detail which in our view did not exist before, we suddenly discover that it is a rare gem." It is with just such intense attention that Michèle Mairot, Sonia Salvi and Laurence Beuvelet decorate Jaeger-LeCoultre movements: so that each detail becomes a source of wonderment.

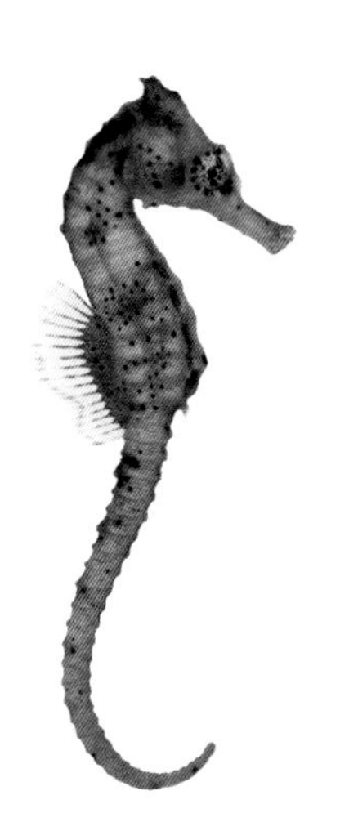

VIII

Reverso Gran'Sport

On the other side of sport, an art of living

Reverso Gran'Sport

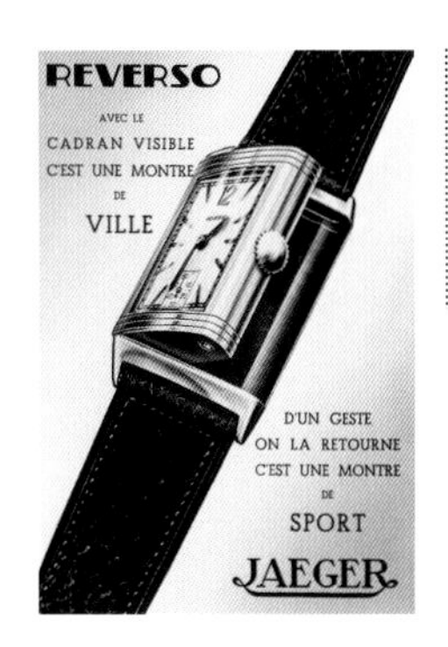

Merging sport and elegance within a single watch. A concept that already made its mark on time in 1931.

The development of sports activities necessitated the creation of a sturdy watch. Although inspired by English polo players, the "swivel watch" also appealed to those who enjoyed other sports.

In the late 19th century, men generally wore only pocket-watches; while these were indeed stylish timekeepers, they were rather limited in practical terms. Moreover, the first rectangular wristwatches of the early 20th century, initially intended for ladies, quickly began to appeal to men also. Time, an indispensable tool in planning one's day, needed to be available in a practical form so that everyone could measure it as they wished. Thus, by 1930, men's wristwatches became a more widespread phenomenon.

Very rapidly, wristwatches became part of daily life. To be able to read the time in every situation, they needed to accompany each of our movements, each of our actions. The development of sports activities required the creation of increasingly sturdy watches. It was specifically in response to the request of English polo players that Jaeger-LeCoultre created the Reverso in 1931. The wristwatches of the time were too delicate for such a virile sport: their crystals, in particular, rarely survived the shocks and jarring involved in a polo, golf or tennis match. The idea of a reversible case was born, a watch that swivelled to protect it from any inadvertent damage. Now, building on its rich past, it is turning towards new vistas of liberty. Always ready to measure up to the most widely practised sports, and representative of a refined style suited to all circumstances, the Reverso has found its way unerringly through decades of changing trends and fashions. There is a vast world on the other side of sport, one of space, freedom and strong emotions. On the other side of sport lies the pursuit of true happiness, the art of living well at the present moment. Midway between dreams and reality, this world has now found its watch: the Reverso Gran'Sport. Through this novel concept of the sports watch, the Reverso brings together its most effective assets in a model of impeccable elegance and well-being. In automatic or manually-wound chronograph versions, the Reverso Gran'Sport looks unlike any other watch in the sports world. The Reverso Gran'Sport combines sturdiness and refinement, reliability and comfort, technology and aesthetics: essential criteria for a watch from which one is never separated. Connoisseurs will appreciate its unparalleled performance and the accumulation of details and innovations that make all the difference. This Reverso Gran'Sport is resolutely innovative. Water-resistant to 5 atmospheres, its case is fitted with a system which prevents unwanted swivelling when jarred, and its cambered base guarantees exceptional comfort on the wrist. The automatic model is fitted with a screw-lock crown, while the chronograph has a non-screwed double-gasket crown. Both mechanical movements of the Gran'Sport with large date aperture and 44-hour power-reserve were designed, developed and made at Jaeger-LeCoultre. Manually-wound Calibre 859 powers the

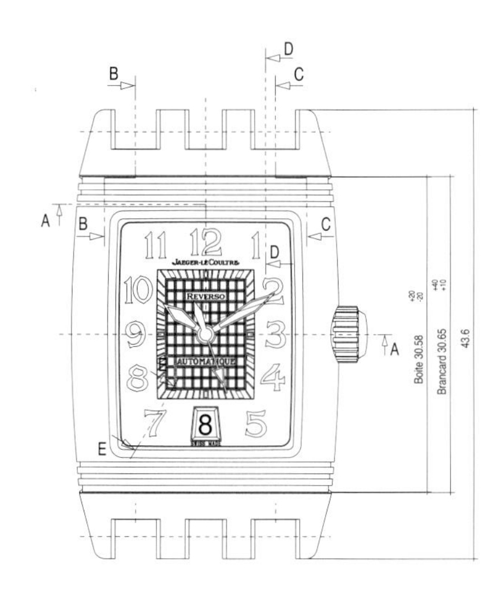

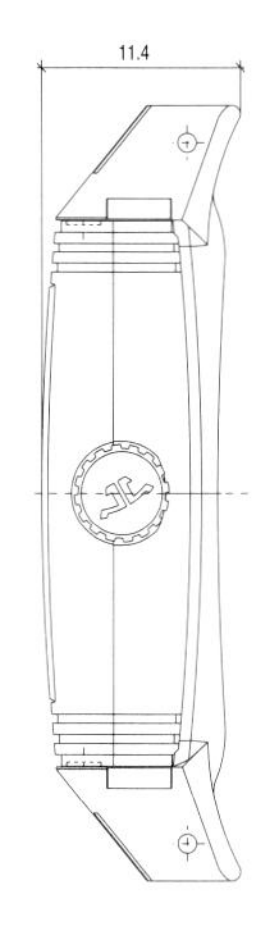

The curved base of the Reverso Gran'Sport makes it exceptionally comfortable to wear.

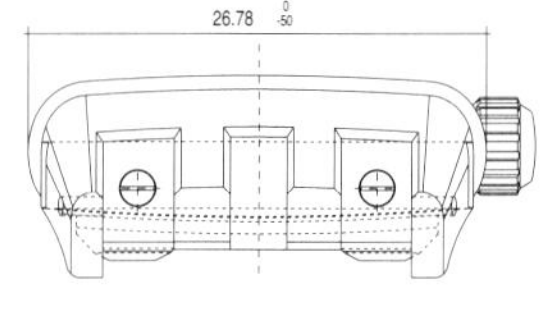

Gran'Sport Chronographe, and Calibre 960R drives the Automatique model.
The integrated bracelet is an exceptional object in its own right. Crafted in gold or steel with individually assembled curved links, it is put together according to a patented Jaeger-LeCoultre concept guaranteeing complete suppleness. Its clasp, made up of 52 parts, is doubtless the most complex in the world. It also has a screw-free double safety opening system with easy length adjustment. The dial underscores the unique temperament of the Reverso Gran'Sport. Silvered or slate-grey, it features grenadier-type guilloché work and Linton numerals. The Automatique displays the hours, minutes and seconds on one side, with large date window at 6 o'clock, while it makes its back available for those who wish to have initials engraved in exclusive Gran'Sport lettering. The Chronographe also has a start/stop shutter ("Marche/Arrêt") for the chronograph function and, on the other side, it shows its capacity for performance with 60-second and 30-minute counters. On one side the Reverso Gran'Sport is a feat of watchmaking technology, and on the other a world that thrives on the intensity of action.

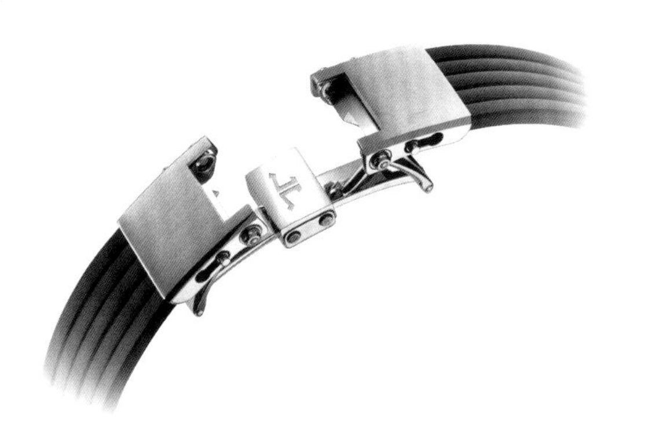

The rubber strap created for the Reverso Gran'Sport is a truly unique object: "One of the greatest strengths of rubber is its exceptional elasticity and its very high resistance to extreme stresses and strains: water, salt, perspiration, wear and tear. In order to create wristbands combining impeccable quality and peerless aesthetic precision, the making of each strap called for a series of meticulous operations. Perfectly in tune with the streamlined appearance of the watch, the black rubber strap with five godrons makes it an even more comfortable fit on the wrist. Light and gentle to the touch, sturdy and featuring refined details, it merges sport and elegance in an distinctly avant-garde style. We have designed a dedicated clasp for this model, made up of 38 parts. As on the steel bracelet, this patented Jaeger-LeCoultre clasp is fitted with a screw-free double safety system providing the same easy summer/winter or morning/evening adjustment over a length of 2 x 4 mm."

Francis Cretin / Design-engineer

One in rubber, one in steel: the two wristbands of the Reverso Gran'Sport underline the uniquely avant-garde nature of the watch. Combining suppleness with studiness, and comfort with security, they are both fitted with an adjustable folding clasp, allowing you to experience the full intensity the moment.

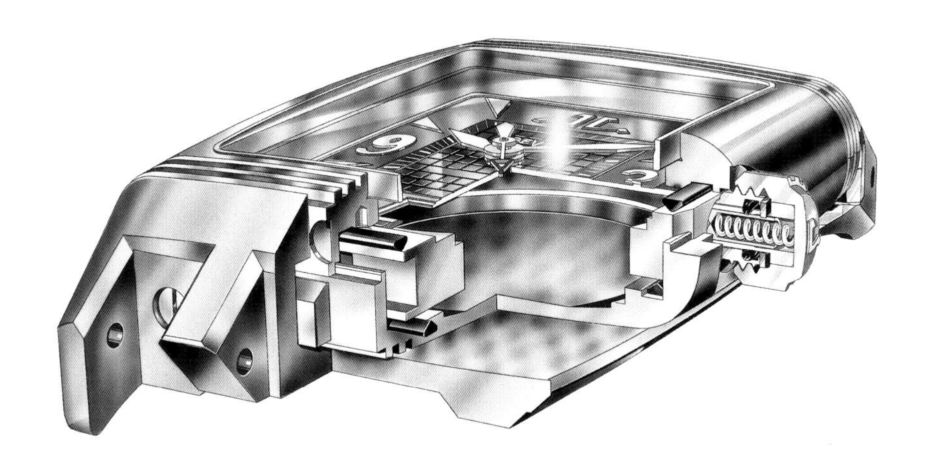

Cross-section of the Reverso Gran'Sport Automatique: screw-locked crown with double protection against infiltration, specifically shaped water-resistance joints and scratch-resistant sapphire crystal fitted on shaped gasket.

To accompany its owner to the heart of action, the Reverso Gran'Sport had to provide faultless reliability, so Jaeger-LeCoultre took its pursuit of water-resistance further than ever. Daniel Wild demonstrates the care devoted to achieving perfection in each detail. "Not only has the gasket been placed in a groove machined with extreme precision, but the shape has been carefully rounded in the angles to obtain optimal water-resistance in each corner of the part." This calls for first-quality joints and an extreme degree of meticulousness at all stages of manufacturing, from stamping to machining through to moulding. "It takes almost twenty operations, step by step, to reach perfect forming, a groove with not even the slightest fissure in the joint recess. The machining surface in the groove is almost polished in order to avoid any infiltration." Daniel underscores that even the crystal is fitted in a shaped joint in order to guarantee perfect water-resistance. " The nylon of this joint serves as a buffer between metal and crystal, thereby compensating for differences in dilatation." Another water-resistance factor is that all parts involved in swivelling the case are in stainless steel or are protected by dipping in a galvanic bath. Finally, Daniel wants connoisseurs to know about a specific additional security detail. "The Reverso Gran'Sport is fitted with a double-gasket crown, which is screwed for the automatic version, while an ingenious system makes it easy to replace the water-resistance joints for pushpieces in its chronograph version."

Daniel Wild / Design-engineer

Encounter an exceptional world

Reverso Gran'Sport Chronographe

The Reverso Gran'Sport Chronographe houses Calibre 859 by Jaeger-LeCoultre, a masterpiece of watchmaking tradition embodied in a mechanical, manually-wound movement. Like all exceptional individuals, the Reverso Gran'Sport Chronographe does not reveal all its assets on the first encounter.

Reverso Gran'Sport Chronographe.
Stainless steel.
Rubber strap.

295 86 50 (M)
Calibre 859.

Reverso Gran'Sport
Chronographe.
Stainless steel.

295 81 20 (M)
Calibre 859.

The Chronograph mechanism in the "stop" position.
The start/stop indication on the front sign do the state of the Chronograph function.

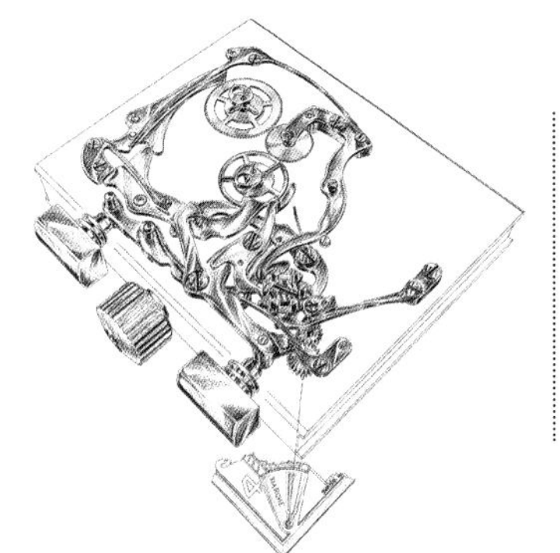

The chronograph mechanism in the "start" position. These levers, gear-trains and heart-pieces handle the chronograph functions. Somewhat resembling a crenellated tower, the column-wheel coordinates and synchronises all the lever movements.

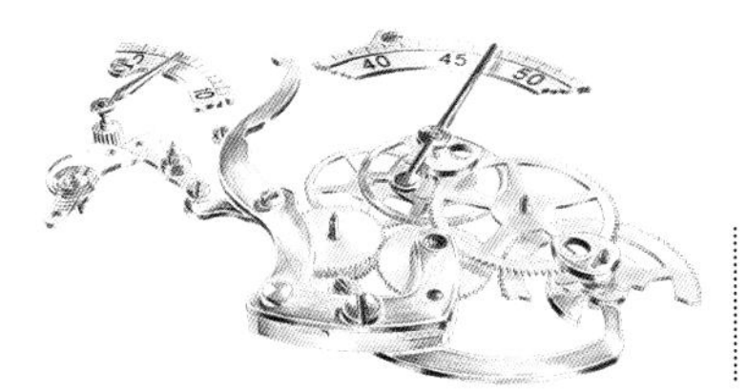

Gear-train driving the seconds counter and the retrograde minutes counter.

This technical drawing highlights the complexity of the rectangular chronograph movement of the Reverso Gran'Sport and gives a glimpse of the balance as well as the many levers and gear-trains of the chronograph mechanism.

Reverso Gran'Sport Chronographe.
18-carat yellow gold.

295 16 20 (M)
Calibre 859.

Reverso Gran'Sport Chronographe.
18-carat yellow gold.
Rubber strap with yellow gold Gran'Sport clasp.

295 16 20 (M)
Calibre 859.

A world
of performance in
pleasurable form

Reverso Gran'Sport Automatique

Cambered case, guilloché dial displaying the date and an amazingly supple and comfortable bracelet. The Reverso Gran'Sport Automatique opens up a world of its own just for you. A world of pleasure... and extreme refinement.

Reverso Gran'Sport Automatique.
Stainless steel.
Rubber strap.

290 86 50 (A)
Calibre 960R.

The Reverso Gran'Sport Automatique beats to the rhythm of Calibre 960R. This is the first time that a mechanical automatic movement has been fitted within a Jaeger-LeCoultre swivel case.

Reverso Gran'Sport Automatique.
Stainless steel.

290 81 20 (A)
Calibre 960R.

Reverso Gran'Sport Automatique.
18-carat yellow gold.

290 11 20 (A)
Calibre 960R.

Reverso Gran'Sport Automatique.
18-carat yellow gold.
Rubber strap with yellow gold Gran'Sport clasp.

290 16 20 (A)
Calibre 960R.

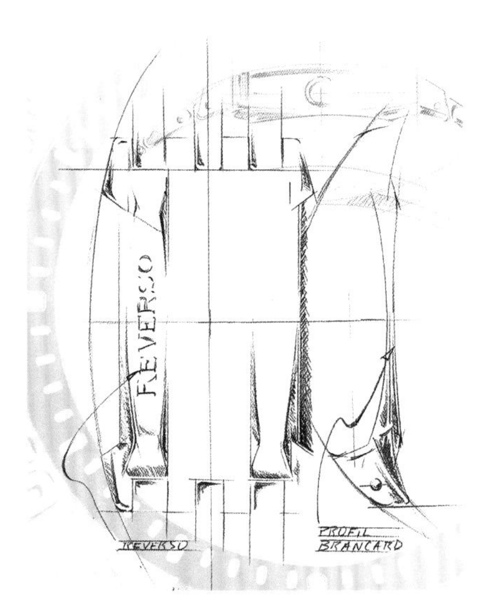

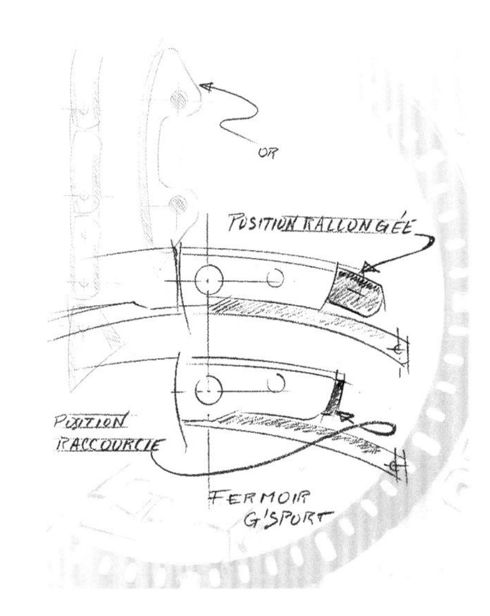

After integrating the various complications in the history of watchmaking into the Reverso models, Jaeger-LeCoultre wished to create new, contemporary, practical and active ones. The idea was to respond to the demands of today's world, while maintaining the volumes and technical features of the Reverso, remaining in harmony with the standards of fine watchmaking. So, when looking at sport, Reverso turned to another dimension, and its designer, Janek Deleskiewicz, imagined a new concept. "The aim was to take the Reverso into an as yet unexplored lifestyle: more sportswear oriented, with no constraints, where one takes the time to forget time and times. In order not to simply endure time, one must forget one's watch. The Reverso Gran'Sport could be seen as our return to the future: Jaeger-LeCoultre is in no way abandoning the legend of the Reverso, but is conferring on it all the assets it will need to move unscathed through time while heralding the future. On an aesthetic level, I renounced any unjustified artifices in order to reach a design in which the form arises from the function. It is above all its efficiency which makes the Gran'Sport truly beautiful." However, while aesthetics were definitely determined by function, the Reverso Gran'Sport has no shortage of charms: "I left plenty of space for dreams, poetry, and a good share of emotion and authenticity. This watch has a soul and it encapsulates the feelings of all those who played their part in making it."

Janek Deleskiewicz / Designer

Beyond sport,
the feminine art of
elegant living

Reverso Gran'Sport Lady

The Reverso Gran'Sport Lady embodies a new feminine passion: a multi-faceted timekeeper which enriches the performances of a sports watch with notions such as dream-like elegance and constantly renewed pleasure.

The Reverso Gran'Sport Lady achieves a new performance in the sports watch category. It reflects an art of living that combines charm and technology, to accompany 21st century women wherever they may go.

After pioneering a new era in men's sports watches, the Reverso Gran'Sport is turning its talents to the art of living in the feminine mode. Whether for elegant or leisure wear, business life or daydreaming, the Reverso Gran'Sport Lady is a first-rate companion to accompany 21st century women, by day or night, here or elsewhere.

Achieving a new performance in the sports category, enabling ladies watches to exercise all their charms? A challenge to which the Jaeger-LeCoultre master-watchmakers have risen with panache. Finally, the polar opposites of sport and elegance, sturdiness and refinement are united within in a single timekeeper. It embodies a new art of living offering women a broad range of pleasures. The Reverso Gran'Sport Lady combines all the assets of the masculine model that inspired it, representing an unparalleled feat of form and function through the accumulation of unusual details. The cambered reversible case is fitted with a system guaranteeing that it locks when jarred.

Combining strength and character, it is placed on a curved carrier that ensures exceptional wearer comfort. In technical and performance terms, the Reverso Gran'Sport Lady, water-resistant to 50 metres, ranks among the most competitive in its discipline. Mechanically driven by Jaeger-LeCoultre Calibre 864, it features a dual time-zone display and a power-reserve of 50 hours. In addition to showing the hours, minutes and small seconds at 6 o'clock, it differentiates between day and night, for women who

"Above and beyond its legendary duality, the Reverso Gran'Sport Lady offers women a multi-faceted world. It is the companion of the most striking paradoxes, the reflection of daily life in which it moves seamlessly from work to leisure activities. Understated and sporting, or elegant and precious, it is ready to adapt to any situation, in a simple turn of its swivel case. The diamond-set face underlines the "easy to wear" nature of steel and the extreme refinement of jewellery. Endowed with a second time-zone display, the Reverso Gran'Sport Lady allows its wearer to keep a finger on the pulse of the whole world. Technical watchmaking is also a feminine value."

Magali Métrailler / Designer

live outside of spatio-temporal constraints. The front shows the time here and now, while the back displays the time elsewhere at the very same moment... Being in synchrony with the four corners of the world is also the new art of keeping in step with the times. Fired by passion and inspired by great dreams, the Reverso Gran'Sport Lady matches the performances of its functions with the matchless comfort of its patented bracelet and clasp, endowed with the same qualities as the men's version: the incomparable suppleness and reliability of finely curved metal links; easy summer/winter adjustment; and the security of a double-blade folding clasp. Despite all these technical accomplishments drawn from the masculine version, the Reverso Gran'Sport Lady is nonetheless every inch a woman. Especially on the back, where it fulfils its desire for exclusive elegance: 32 diamonds set horizontally on the case underline the delicate floral numerals, sparkling on its silvered dial. Crafted in steel or 18-carat gold, this horological "force of nature" lends itself willingly to a feminine approach to experiencing elegance in all circumstances. Unique in its kind, the Reverso Gran'Sport Lady signals a new era in the history of ladies sports watches: from now on, they will have no cause to be jealous of their masculine counterparts.

Reverso Gran'Sport Lady.
Stainless steel
set with diamonds.

296 81 20 (M)
Calibre 864.

Reverso Gran'Sport Lady.
18-carat yellow gold set with diamonds.

296 11 20 (M)
Calibre 864.

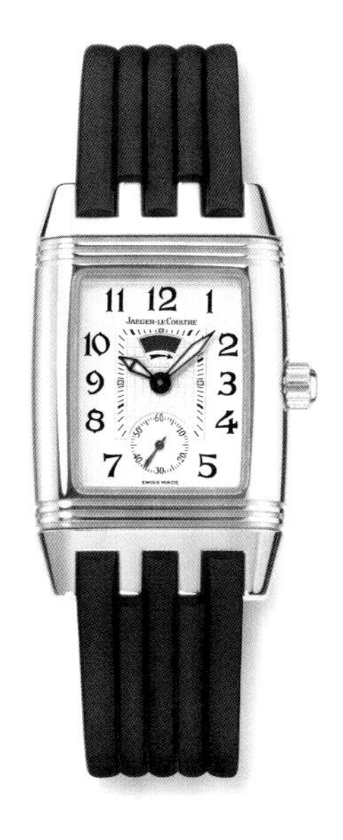

Reverso Gran'Sport Lady.
Stainless steel
set with diamonds.
Rubber strap.

296 86 20 (M)
Calibre 864.

Reverso Gran'Sport Lady.
18-carat yellow gold
set with diamonds.
Rubber strap with yellow gold
Gran'Sport clasp.

296 16 20 (M)
Calibre 864.

"Merging into reality in order to fulfill a dream is the surest way of finding the key to truth. The absolute is not accessible, but by modelling one's conceptions on the patterns of nature, mankind can get extremely close. Creativity starts with the pursuit of symbiosis between the universe and uniqueness." Daniel Wild and Francis Cretin clothe each timekeeper in accordance with its own specific nature, by seeking the technical and aesthetic means to give it an unmistakably personal identity...

NOV
JAN
MAR
SEP
JUL
MAY
SUN
MON
TUE
WED
THU
FRI
JAEGER-LECOULTRE
6

12
9
3
6
JAEGER-LECOULTRE

IX

Master Control 1000 Hours

A new standard of reference

Master Control 1000 Hours

In creating the first automatic alarm wristwatch, Jaeger-LeCoultre was introducing an outstanding innovation in watchmaking history. Witness this advertisement from the 1950s.

Never accepting half-measures, whether in terms of reliability or creativity, has always been a question of principle for Jaeger-LeCoultre. In launching the Master Control 1000 Hours test, the Manufacture established a new benchmark of watchmaking quality.

The Master Control 1000 Hours principle is based on an exceptionally stringent battery of tests. Never before had anyone subjected its wristwatches to 1000 hours of testing. Launched in 1992, the Master Grande Taille gave rise to entire line of time-keepers that now stand as the very embodiment of an authentic man's wristwatch. They recall the not so distant time when the rhythm of life was based on the precision and reliability of mechanical watchmaking, and bear a distinct likeness to the great Jaeger-LeCoultre successes of the 1950s: the Memovox, the Futurematic or the Geomatic. However, it is not only their nostalgic charm that arouses such

Swiss watchmaking at its best: the 1962 wristwatch chronometer Geomatic shown above epitomizes the ideal of the perfect mechanical watch. The Master watch, brought out in 1992 with the Calibre 889, follows on in this tradition.

enthusiasm for Master Control watches. Jaeger-LeCoultre's primary goal in creating the Master Control was to impose a new benchmark for reliability. Each watch undergoes a rigorous schedule of tests. Before being deemed worthy to carry the Master Control label, each finished watch must go through 1000 hours of the strictest testing. This series of tests implies a level of requirements far higher than an official timekeeping test, which only deals with the movement. For Jaeger-LeCoultre, it is the finished, fully cased-up watch complete with dial and hands that is tested. The entire watch is tested in six positions, while rotating and when at rest. It is faced with calculated shocks and water-resistance is tested up to 5 atmospheres. It must also stand up to a wide range of temperatures. This series of trials which challenges all aspects of the watch is intended to detect the slightest weakness and to certify its performances. These 1000 first hours of the life of the watch serve as a trustworthy passport for the decades to come.

A steel 7-link bracelet may be fitted on Master Control watches.

Each watch is placed several times on a cyclotest instrument that turns 800 times in two hours, throughout the Master Control 1000 Hours testing period. This test guarantees the smooth operation of the self-winding mechanism of the watch.

Test 1:
Places the Master Control watch on a machine which imparts a to-and-fro rotating movement and subjects it to a number of the kind of light calculated shocks typical of daily use, automatically rewinding it. The goal of this test is to check that the mainspring shows a normal degree of tension and to ensure that all watch components are correctly fixed in their appointed place.

Test 2:
Is intended to check the perfect adjustment of the balance-spring, which returns the balance to its position of equilibrium, ensures equal oscillations and governs the regularity of rate of the watch. The measurement is based on tests performed in 6 different positions simulating conditions of regular wear.

Test 3:
Allows watchmakers to check the power-reserve, meaning the time it takes for the mainspring to release its energy and ensure the watch continues to function independently.

Test 4:
Confirms the resistance to variations in temperature of the metal alloy used for the balance-spring. If it dilates, this would affect the reliability of the watch. The test is carried out in the kind of extreme weather conditions which the Master Control might have to face when worn. After being placed at a room temperature of 22°C, it is moved to an environment at 4°C, meaning a difference of 18°C. Finally, it has to withstand a temperature of 40°C inside a special case.

Each watch to emerge successfully from the Master Control 1000 Hours trial is awarded a certificate from the master-watchmaker responsible. This "diploma" proves that the watch has undergone the six tests and that it is worthy of the highest trust.

Test 5:
Is carried out on the cyclotest machine, which reproduces the many movements implied by daily wear on the wrist: for three weeks, the watch alternates rotating movements with periods of rest. By the end of this test, the longest in the Master Control series, the smooth running of the watch can be fully guaranteed.

Test 6:
Aims to ensure that the watch is water-resistant to a depth of 5 atm and is thus protected from any intrusions. Two tests confirm this total water-tightness of the Master Control and the infallibility of its water-tightness gaskets. In the air test, a watch is placed under pressure in a defined volume: any variation in volume would warn of a possible leak. After 1000 hours of testing carried out over a six-week period, the watch movement is perfectly well run-in and prepared to face whatever challenges may arise.

The numbered gold seal on the case-back is the visible guarantee that the Master Control has passed its 1,000-hour test.

Excellence summed up in 6 exceptional masterpieces

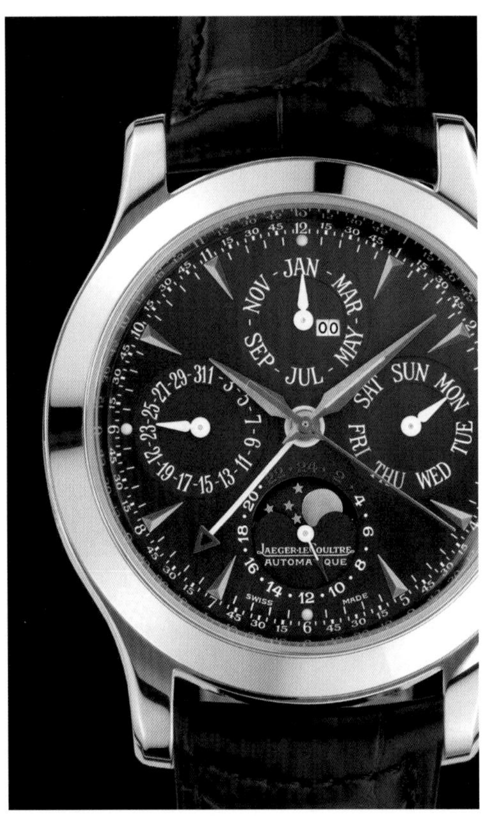

Master Limited series in platinum

The understated, authentic refinement of platinum highlights the complexity and rarity of the Master Grande Memovox issued in a limited edition of 250. Its deep blue dial enhances the value of its complications: alarm and perpetual calendar.

To emphasize the accomplishments of the Master Control 1000 Hours line, and to match excellence of function by that of matter: such was the wish of the master-watchmakers at Jaeger-LeCoultre. They chose platinum to clothe the technical complexity and aesthetic power of these timekeepers. Since 1997, six models in platinum have been crafted in limited series of 250 each.

The first to be chosen were the Master Geographic and the Master Perpetual. After initially appearing in steel or gold cases, they now truly fulfill their promise in a platinum 950 case fitted with a hinged case-back engraved with the words "Série limitée à 250 pièces Platinum". Another shared feature is the deep blue dial which is echoed by a midnight blue crocodile leather strap fitted with a platinum folding buckle. In 1999, adorned with the same characteristics, two other models merged the benchmark quality of

In 1992, the alarm and perpetual calendar functions were brought together within the Grand Réveil model in platinum by Jaeger-LeCoultre. Today, the Master Grande Memovox echoes this accomplishment, once again entrancing collectors.

"Série limitée à 250 pièces": this engraving in Anglaise lettering on the hinged case-back underscores the rare nature of the Master Moon in platinum. Behind this "window" in the case, admirers can gaze at the beauty of Jaeger-LeCoultre Calibre 891/448/2.

their movement with the supremacy of the noblest of metals. Master Moon and Master Réserve de Marche joined the lineage of Limited series in platinum. They were followed in 2001 by two unique models from the Manufacture: the Master Ultra Thin and the Master Grande Memovox. These last two possess the same attributes for which the previous Limited series in platinum have become known and recognized, with one exception: they do not have a hinged case-back. The Master Ultra Thin invites connoisseurs to observe the mechanical feats performed by its movement through a sapphire back, while the Master Grande Memovox jealously protects the ultimate alliance between alarm mechanism and perpetual calendar by a solid back. Naturally, these exceptional series fully comply with the rules of the Master Control 1000 Hours test; they have successfully and uncompromisingly undergone the same trials as the original models. In this manner, Jaeger-LeCoultre's tireless pursuit of excellence fulfills collectors' desires by uniting the world of fine watchmaking with that of useful and sophisticated complications.

Master Grande Memovox.
2001.
950 platinum.
Crocodile strap with
platinum folding buckle.

146 64 8/A/F/D (A)
Calibre 909.
Limited series of 250.

Master Ultra Thin.
2001.
950 platinum.
Sapphire-crystal case-back.
Crocodile strap with
platinum buckle.

145 64 80 (M)
Calibre 849.
Limited series of 250.

Master Réserve de Marche.
1999.
950 platinum.
Hinged case-back.
Crocodile strap with
platinum folding buckle.

148 64 80 (A)
Calibre 928.
Limited series of 250.

Master Moon.
1999.
950 platinum.
Hinged case-back.
Crocodile strap with
platinum folding buckle.

143 64 8A/F/D (A)
Calibre 891/448/2.
Limited series of 250.

Master Perpetual.
1997.
950 platinum.
Hinged case-back.
Crocodile strap with
platinum folding buckle.

149 64 8A/F/D (A)
Calibre 889/440/2.
Limited series of 250.

Master Geographic.
1997.
950 platinum.
Hinged case-back.
Crocodile strap with
platinum folding buckle.

142 64 80 (A)
Calibre 929/3.
Limited series of 250.

Two virtuosos of time in perfect harmony

Master Grande Memovox

The Master Grande Memovox constitutes the crowning glory of the Master Control line, providing a brilliant combination of two virtuoso time functions.

1962. Memovox with alarm and date. Jaeger-LeCoultre Calibre 911, a mechanical manually-wound movement.

Born of the genius of the Manufacture, the Master Grande Memovox is the matchless repository of rare and specific talents: the combination of perpetual calendar and alarm.

Each function of the Master Grande Memovox represents the expression of perfectly accomplished mastery. The perpetual calendar is one of the most complex and elaborate refinements within the repertory of horological miniaturization. It is mechanically programmed to display the year, the month, the date, the day, the moon phases and the 24 hours, along with a red security-zone indication. Meanwhile, the alarm function, historically a Jaeger-LeCoultre speciality, embodies the secrets of metallurgical alchemy to give the chime the purity it requires. A tiny hammer strikes a gong

Made up of 349 parts, Jaeger-LeCoultre Calibre 909 combines two sovereign watchmaking complications: a perpetual calendar mechanism and an alarm chiming on a gong. The destiny of the Master Grande Memovox is to give visible and audible cadence to the rhythms of eternity.

1989. Grand Réveil.
Perpetual calendar
and striking mechanism
on bronze bell.

suspended from the inner rim of the case-back, causing it to vibrate and emit a crystal-clear sound wave. Fitted with automatic Jaeger-LeCoultre Calibre 909, the Master Grande Memovox represents a culminating splendour entirely in keeping with the spirit of the Master Control line: a sovereign alliance of two useful and perfectly complementary functions; complex mechanisms interpreted through simple and user-friendly handling; the whole governed by consistent respect for aesthetic understatement. The autonomy of functions reveals the uncompromising quest for efficiency that guided the master-watchmakers. Two crowns perform their own specific set of functions: one is used to adjust the hours, minutes and date; while the other winds, sets, starts and stops the alarm. The alarm winding mechanism is independent from the movement winding mechanism, thereby ensuring a power-reserve of around 45 hours. The information provided by the perpetual calendar is adjusted by means of a single corrector at 8 o'clock: one press moves the calendar functions simultaneously and swiftly forward in one-day units. To accommodate the 349 components of Calibre 909, the Master Grande Memovox has been given a slightly larger case than the other Master Control models. Moreover, like its exceptional counterparts, it has passed the merciless scrutiny of the Master Control 1000 Hours tests with flying colours.

Master Grande Memovox.
18-carat pink gold.
Crocodile strap with
pink gold folding buckle.

146 24 2A/F/D (A)
Calibre 909.

Compared with its forerunner, the Grand Réveil, the Master Grande Memovox has honed its function to achieve even greater reliability, despite the limited space available within the watch: "Rapid adjustments were previously made by a pushpiece integrated within the crown. For aesthetic reasons and to ensure greater security, we managed to integrate it within the watch case itself, at 10 o'clock. Thanks to the principle of the "all or nothing function", adjustments are simplified to the extreme. Thus, without the help of a calendar, one can correct the day, date, month and moon-phase indications using a single pushpiece. Moreover, the Master Grande Memovox guarantees a power-reserve of at least 48 hours."

Manel Guérin / Master-watchmaker

Only eternity lasts longer

Master Perpetual

It takes no less than the 277 parts of Calibre 889/440/2 for the Master Perpetual to effortless display – in addition to the hours, minutes and seconds – the date, day, month, year, decade and moon phases.

The date indicator automatically accounts for months of 28, 29, 30 or 31 days.

Clearly visible, even when the sky is clouded: the moon-phase display.

Safety device: when the red mark appears in the aperture, do not adjust your calendar.

Like all perpetual calendars, the Master Perpetual has a self-adjusting date. That means the mechanism knows whether there are 28, 30 or 31 days in the current month, and it will remember to show February 29 each leap year.

In addition, it shows the day, the month, the year, the decade, the phase of the moon and, of course, the hours, minutes and seconds. There is one snag though. A watchmaker will have to reset the calendar to the 400-year cycle of the secular leap year on Monday, March 1, 2100. In the Master Control perpetual-calendar watch, "perpetual" is the operative word. It should be working well when it is taken in for that adjustment a century or more hence. All functions are controlled using two parts: a single winding-crown – which you will only rarely use for actually rewinding, since the Master Perpetual houses an automatic movement – and a pushpiece mechanism which enables you to reprogram the entire calendar. This astonishing ease of handling is coupled with unparalleled reliability. The 277 parts comprising the automatic movement and calendar mechanism have been finished, polished and fitted by hand to ensure smooth, precise operation. Then the watch is thoroughly tested. For six continuous weeks its performance is monitored as it encounters every hazard it is expected to live through: temperature extremes, shocks, pressures equivalent to 50 metres under water and constant motion. 1,000 hours of rigourous testing: essential when eternity is at stake.

Master Perpetual.
18-carat pink gold.
Crocodile strap with
pink gold folding buckle.

149 24 2A/F/D (A)
Calibre 889/440/2.

Master Perpetual.
18-carat white gold.
Hinged case-back.
crocodile strap with
white gold folding buckle.

149 34 4A/F/D (A)
Calibre 889/440/2.

Master Perpetual.
Stainless steel.
Crocodile strap
with folding buckle.

149 84 2A/F/D (A)
Calibre 889/440/2.

Master Perpetual.
Stainless steel.
Crocodile strap
with folding buckle.

149 84 7A/F/D (A)
Calibre 889/440/2.

The Maltese cross incorporated within the calendar has enabled the Master Perpetual to follow the passing years without any hitches whatsoever. Its mechanical automatic movement is thus equipped to run for many decades.

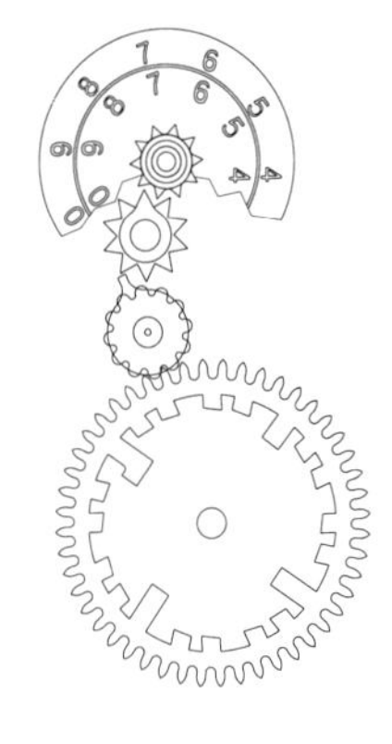

Before

After

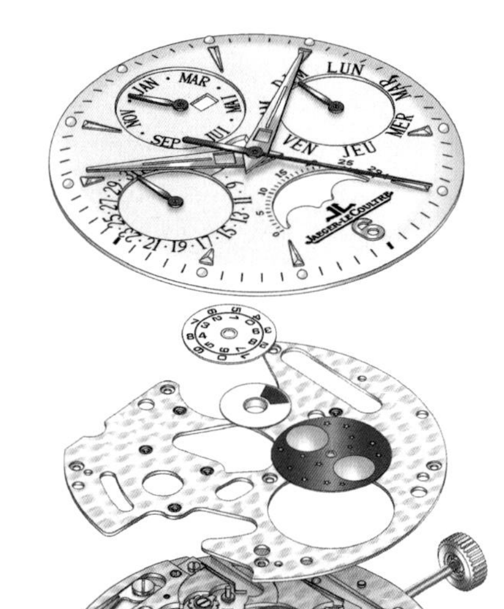

"Our perpetual calendar has a single corrector pushpiece for moon-phase, day, date, month, year and decade functions, all of which are mechanically programmed. This requires great exactitude in assembling the calendar in order to avoid any time-lag", explains Christian Laurent, the master-watchmaker responsible for Jaeger-LeCoultre complications. "Adjusting the passage of the years and decades caused us many sleepless nights... we had to solve the problem, once and for all. I got my team together for a brainstorming session and we found a solution: fitting the internal year wheel with new toothing. In reality, this "Maltese cross" toothing had been discovered long since by our forefathers. Since then, our calendars no longer show any time-lag and allow us to sleep in peace."

Christian Laurent / Master-watchmaker

"The fruit of nature and human culture, individuals are shaped by absorbing the emotions surrounding them. Thus, caught between earth and air, fire and water, they merge into the universe to mould their soul and sculpt their talents. The strength of their experiences transmits the most precious wealth of knowledge, so that it can become the driving force of other generations." The apprentices at Jaeger-LeCoultre are heirs to an irreplaceably valuable legacy which they faithfully perpetuate.

Master Geographic

The time in two time-zones from a glance at the dial. City names to be selected and 24-hour indication for the second time-zone: Jaeger-LeCoultre has provided a clever and elegant solution to the problem of arranging a dial carrying multiple time-zone displays.

This tiny pushpiece is for setting the date, using a stylus supplied with the watch.

One crown is all it takes to wind the movement, set local time and synchronize the second time-zone.

This crown moves the time-zone disc, to show the local time in the selected city, indicating whether it is day or night.

In designing and producing the Master Geographic with its multiple time-zones, the master-watchmakers of Jaeger-LeCoultre have added a genuine masterpiece to their record of achievements.

This multi-talented watch simultaneously indicates local time and that of any other point on the globe, while providing a day/night display. These functions are enriched by the date and an indication of power-reserve, a major first in such a complicated automatic watch. This timekeeper for globetrotters is equipped with another unique feature: the rotating disc which makes it possible to select a city representative of the chosen time-zone in the aperture located at 6 o'clock. It is coupled with a dial below which gives the time in the time-zone selected. An additional aperture specifies whether it is day or night. The Master Geographic is spectacularly easy to use. One simply selects a time-zone by turning the crown at 10 o'clock to a desired city... and the lower dial automatically indicates the corresponding time. The date can be adjusted using a small pushpiece at 2 o'clock. The crown at 3 o'clock makes it possible to set local time and to rewind the watch if it has not been worn for over 38 hours. One should note that if the watch is kept on the wrist, its automatic movement will keep it running indefinitely. Moving from summer time to winter time (and vice versa) is also extremely straightforward. To what better mastery of universal time could one aspire?

The Master Geographic's secret:
the miniaturized ball-bearing mechanism
linking the adjustable time-zone disc
to the corresponding local times.

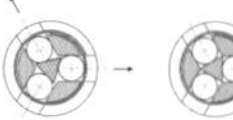
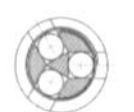
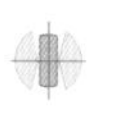

Patented mechanism
of the Master
Geographic.

Master Geographic.
18-carat pink gold.
Crocodile strap with
pink gold folding buckle.

142 24 20 (A)
Calibre 929/3.

Master Geographic.
18-carat white gold.
Hinged case-back.
crocodile strap with
white gold folding buckle.

142 34 40 (A)
Calibre 929/3.

Master Geographic.
Stainless steel.
Crocodile strap
with folding buckle.

142 84 20 (A)
Calibre 929/3.

Master Geographic.
Stainless steel.
Crocodile strap
with folding buckle.

142 84 70 (A)
Calibre 929/3.

"At the dawn of watchmaking history, artisans created their timekeepers by following the biorhythms of nature. Illuminated by the white light of winter, they sat at their workbenches to craft the gear-trains that by spring would give life to new mechanisms." This passion, which was formerly a pastime, has become an exceptional art in its own right. A speciality in which Christian Laurent, Manel Guérin and Joël Viot are accomplished masters, and which is encapsulated in the complications of the Manufacture.

Moons, months and days: a sky-high vision of your life

Master Moon

In the firmament of fine watchmaking, Master Moon is definitely a rising star. Its automatic movement guides you through the spheres of days, months and moons, enabling you to follow the unceasing celestial cadence of the heavenly bodies.

This 1946 men's watch is in keeping with the tradition of moon-phase models. Fitted with Calibre 494, it echoes the classic Jaeger-LeCoultre positioning of date, day of the week and month indications.

In the early 16th century, interest in astronomy had developed so strongly that people wished to carry the newly acquired knowledge around with them.

The increasingly widespread pendant-watches of the Renaissance period were the ideal answer, as they indicated not only the time, but also the date, the day of the week, the month and often even the phases of the moon. The sheer popularity of these functions, rather than their actual necessity, has led watchmakers over the centuries to continue to incorporate them within their creations. Jaeger-LeCoultre perpetuated this tradition in its pocket-watches and was quick to integrate it within its wristwatches from the 1940s onwards.

Within the Jaeger-LeCoultre collection of watches with moon-phase display, a men's model dating from 1949, featuring a calendar and housing Calibre 486. The month and day of the week are shown through two apertures placed side by side.

Master Moon.
18-carat pink gold.
Crocodile strap with
pink gold folding buckle.

143 24 2A/F/D (A)
Calibre 891/448/2.

Master Moon.
18-carat white gold.
Hinged case-back.
Crocodile strap
with white gold
folding buckle.

143 34 4A/F/D (A)
Calibre 891/448/2.

Master Moon.
Stainless steel.
Crocodile strap
with folding buckle.

143 84 2A/F/D (A)
Calibre 891/448/2.

Master Moon.
Stainless steel.
Crocodile strap
with folding buckle.

143 84 7A/F/D (A)
Calibre 891/448/2.

Mastering reliability, day by day

Master Date

The dependability of Jaeger-LeCoultre's Master Date has been perfected by 50 years of experience in date watches, and assured by the comprehensive 1,000-hour test on each watch.

These Day-Date models, first made in the 1940s, provided the inspiration for the Master Date.

Although its design is inspired by the large Jaeger-LeCoultre calendar wristwatches of the forties and fifties, the Master Date is far more than a nostalgic throwback.

Maintaining its longstanding position in the very forefront of watchmaking technology, the Manufacture has created a new high-performance automatic movement for this key model in its Master Control line. The 36-jewel Calibre 891/447 is made up of 270 parts, entirely finished and assembled by hand, including a 22-carat gold oscillating weight segment. To provide you with the assurance of its exemplary reliability, the watch has successfully undergone the full rigours of the Master Control 1000 Hours testing procedure.

The Jaeger-LeCoultre Master Date brings together more than 300 case and movement parts into time-keeping unity. Each part has been finished to tolerances of a few thousandths of a millimetre, to work together with the others as a team. The Master Control 1000 Hours test assures the integrity of their performance.

Master Date.
18-carat pink gold.
Crocodile strap with
pink gold folding buckle.

147 24 2A/F/D (A)
Calibre 891/447.

Master Date.
Stainless steel.
Crocodile strap
with folding buckle.

147 84 2A/F/D (A)
Calibre 891/447.

Master Date in white gold:
its hinged case-back allows one
to unveil the technical and
aesthetic masterpiece represented
by Calibre 891/447.

Master Date.
18-carat white gold.
Hinged case-back.
Crocodile strap
with white gold
folding buckle.

147 34 4A/F/D (A)
Calibre 891/447.

Master Réserve de Marche

The power-reserve indicator is one of the most practical and appreciated complications in mechanical watchmaking. With it, the automatic Master Réserve de Marche displays the state of wind of its mainspring barrel.

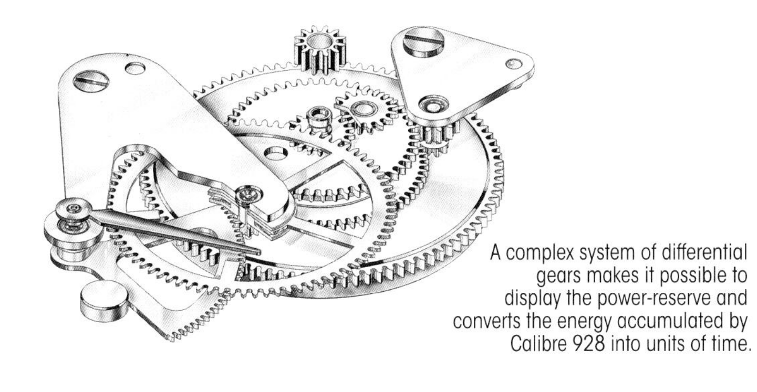

A complex system of differential gears makes it possible to display the power-reserve and converts the energy accumulated by Calibre 928 into units of time.

"In devising the power-reserve for Calibre 928, we wanted to highlight this much sought-after useful complication. We therefore decided to off-centre its aperture by placing it particularly far out towards the rim of the dial. This gives the function a decorative role exuding unprecedented charm. The innovative character and harmonious aesthetic appearance of this positioning make the Master Réserve de Marche a truly exceptional timekeeper."

Rachel Torresani / Design-engineer

For how long will your watch continue to show the time with flawless precision, even if you are not wearing it on your wrist? The Master Réserve de Marche adds a new dimension to the reliability of the Master Control 1000 Hours range.

Jaeger-LeCoultre adds a further dimension to reliability in the Master Réserve de Marche. In addition to the time and date, the dial also shows the amount of power accumulated by the 22-carat gold oscillating weight segment in the 45-jewel, automatic Calibre 928. The power-reserve indicator is a useful reminder of how long your watch will continue to run if it leaves your wrist. But if you continue to wear it, the movement can be relied upon to convert the energy of your gestures into units of time. You can also depend on the 1,000 hours of testing that have ensured the soundness of your watch.

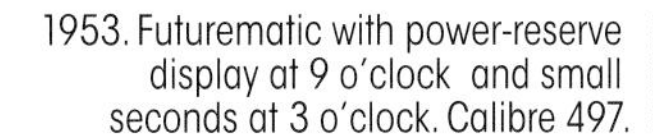

1953. Futurematic with power-reserve display at 9 o'clock and small seconds at 3 o'clock. Calibre 497.

Model available
with silvered dial.
148 84 20 (A)
Calibre 928.

Master Réserve de Marche.
18-carat pink gold.
Crocodile strap with
pink gold folding buckle.

148 24 20 (A)
Calibre 928.

Master Réserve de Marche.
Stainless steel.
Crocodile strap
with folding buckle.

148 84 70 (A)
Calibre 928.

"Both immutable yet adaptable, any living matter is subject to the influence of its environment, so as to be part of the perpetual flow of time. Changing so as to last for a long time while safeguarding one's integrity: such is the key to achieving permanence." This is the law that Thierry Mesnier, Pierre-François Briot and Frédéric Saulcy apply in their electroplating work: a delicate treatment given to certain metal parts of Jaeger-LeCoultre calibres in order to ensure that their coating remains beautiful for many years to come.

Master Réveil

The wrist alarm that rings a bell-like tone is a masterpiece of micro-mechanics and metallurgical skill. It took months to research the optimum shape and positioning of the suspended gong.

Fig. 1

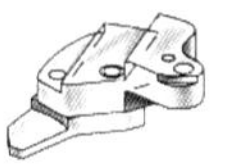

Fig. 2

Fig. 3

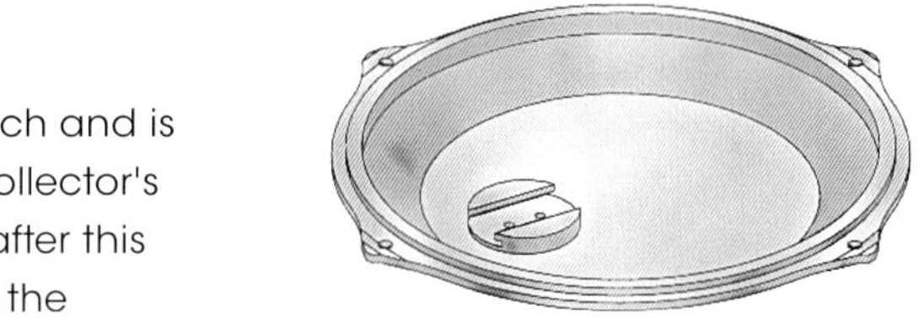

Fig. 4

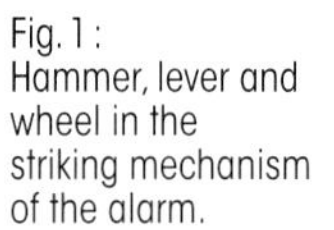

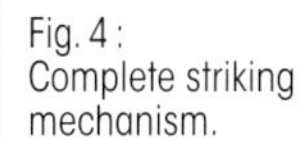

Fig. 1 :
Hammer, lever and wheel in the striking mechanism of the alarm.

Fig. 2 :
Anvil with resonating gong.

Fig. 3 :
Case-back.

Fig. 4 :
Complete striking mechanism.

Thanks to its continuous creativity, Jaeger-LeCoultre has stamped its imprint on a whole range of watchmaking innovations. Witness the 1956 invention of the first automatic alarm wristwatch at the workshops in Le Sentier.

This technical feat was justifiably greeted with enthusiasm, and indeed lovers of fine watchmaking still remember the occasion. An extremely efficient timekeeper, the Master Réveil awoke its wearer from sleep or reminded him or her of an appointment thanks to a hammer striking the inner side of its case. This watch was very popular at the time of its launch and is now a sought-after collector's item. Some 40 years after this spectacular success, the Manufacture has again shown its mettle in creating the automatic Master Réveil, more pleasing to the ear than the original model. The very pure chime, which sounds when the tiny hammer causes the gong suspended inside its case to vibrate, is an

1960. Memovox with alarm, date, and automatic winding.

exceptional combination of effectiveness and discretion. Such sound quality rests on the discovery of a special alloy and the invention of a special shape for the steel gong – a masterpiece attributable to researchers in acoustic metallurgy at Jaeger-LeCoultre. The measurement of time by the Master Réveil is handled by 22-jewel Calibre 918, an automatic movement with a 45-hour power-reserve and a balance oscillating at a rate of 28,800 vibrations/hour. Once cased up, each complete watch must prove its reliability during the rigorous Master Control 1000 Hours test before leaving the workshop. For if we have to interrupt the course of our dreams, it should at least be at the exact time we have chosen...

Master Réveil.
18-carat pink gold.
Crocodile strap with
pink gold folding buckle.

141 24 20 (A)
Calibre 918.

Master Réveil.
Stainless steel.
Crocodile strap
with folding buckle.

141 84 20 (A)
Calibre 918.

Only 4.2 mm thin,
yet tested
to the limit

Master Ultra Thin

Increasing reliability while reducing the thickness of a movement is a task for an horological specialist. The resulting movement passes the 1,000-hour test in the slim case of the Master Ultra Thin.

On the model with a sapphire case-back, an engraving on the movement certifies that the watch has successfully passed the 1,000-hour test procedures.

Normally, the thinner a watch, the simpler and more fragile its movement. The Master Ultra Thin is an exception to this rule. It breaks through the frontiers of the impossible, by pushing mechanical performance to the outer limits of extreme miniaturisation.

Even though the watch measures a mere 4.2 mm high, it still has to go through the full 1,000-hour Master Control reliability test. No concessions are made. Each watch is controlled in six positions, endures calculated shocks, temperature extremes, constant motion and is tested to five atmospheres.

Within the slim case in 18-carat gold or steel, beats a movement that is only 1.85 mm high. The Calibre 849's achievements have won it the respect of watch specialists.

A "thickness" of just 1.38 mm for the world's thinnest mechanical movement.

Model available
with pink gold
folding buckle.
145 24 20 (M)
Calibre 849.

Model available
with white gold
folding buckle.
145 34 40 (M)
Calibre 849.

Master Ultra Thin.
18-carat pink gold.
Crocodile strap with
pink gold buckle.

145 25 20 (M)
Calibre 849.

Master Ultra Thin.
18-carat white gold.
Crocodile strap with
white gold buckle.

145 35 40 (M)
Calibre 849.

Model available
with folding buckle.
145 84 20 (M)
Calibre 849.

Master Ultra Thin.
Stainless steel.
Crocodile strap.

145 85 20 (M)
Calibre 849.

Model available
with folding buckle.
145 84 70 (M)
Calibre 849.

Master Ultra Thin.
Stainless steel.
Crocodile strap.

145 85 70 (M)
Calibre 849.

We make it perfect; then we spend another 1,000 hours making sure

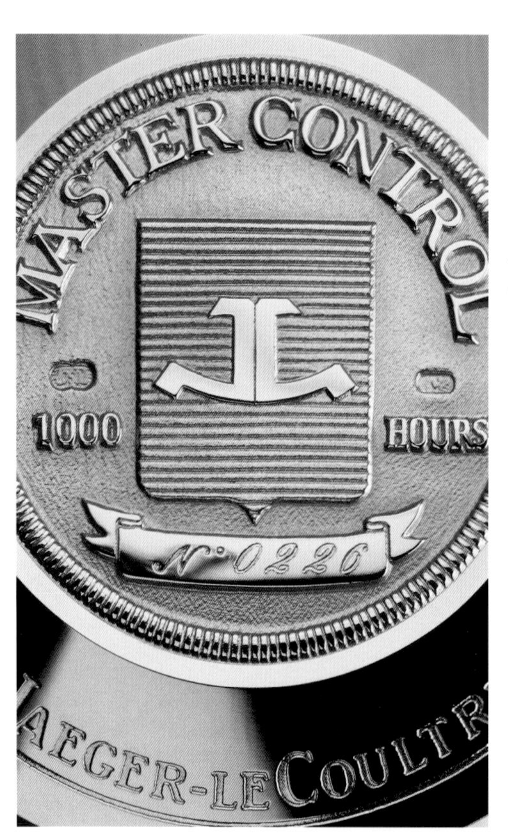

Master Grande Taille

The Master signature: 1,000 hours of rigorous testing and extraordinary reliability, certified by a gold numbered seal on the visible part of the case.

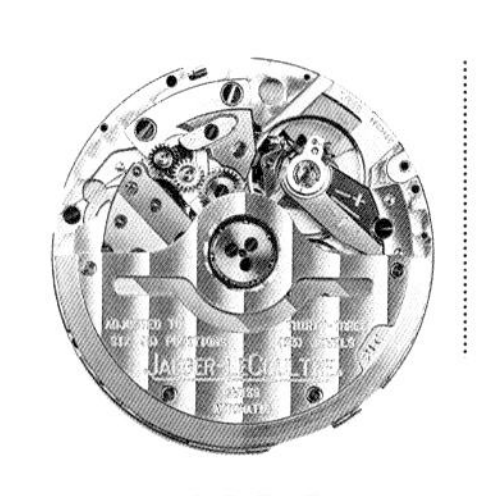

Calibre 889/2. 1994. The high density of 22-carat gold gives the segment of the oscillating weight optimum momentum. A reversing gear transmits its energy to the mainspring, whichever direction it spins.

As the original watch in the Master Collection, the Master Grande Taille sets new standards in the reliability of automatic wristwatches.

Its movement is the remarkable 36-jewel Calibre 889/2 – a fastbeat automatic movement with a balance vibrating at a steady 28,800 semi-oscillations an hour. The 22-carat gold oscillating weight segment converts the slightest motion of the wrist into energy stored in the mainspring barrel. The efficient automatic-winding system keeps the mainspring at constant tension – essential for good time-keeping qualities in a mechanical watch. The complete Master Grande Taille movement consists of 202 parts, each of which has been finished to micron tolerances, polished, fitted and adjusted by hand.

1956. Jaeger-LeCoultre defined the concept of "fully automatic" by omitting the winding crown in the Futurematic model.

Master Grande Taille.
18-carat pink gold.
Crocodile strap with
pink gold folding buckle.

140 24 20 (A)
Calibre 889/2.

Master Grande Taille.
Stainless steel.
Crocodile strap
with folding buckle.

140 84 20 (A)
Calibre 889/2.

"In the beginning was time. Then, flowing from minutes into hours, nights gave way to days, in a cycle of perpetual renewal. Faced with the ongoing flow of time, humankind pondered how to measure such invincible immensity. People learned to fraction the infinitely large into the infinitely small, and ever since have constantly fine-tuned their know-how." Performed by Philippe Hebert, Nadia Gaila and Lydia Pedrina, the Master Control 1000 Hours tests have established a new benchmark in the measurement of time.

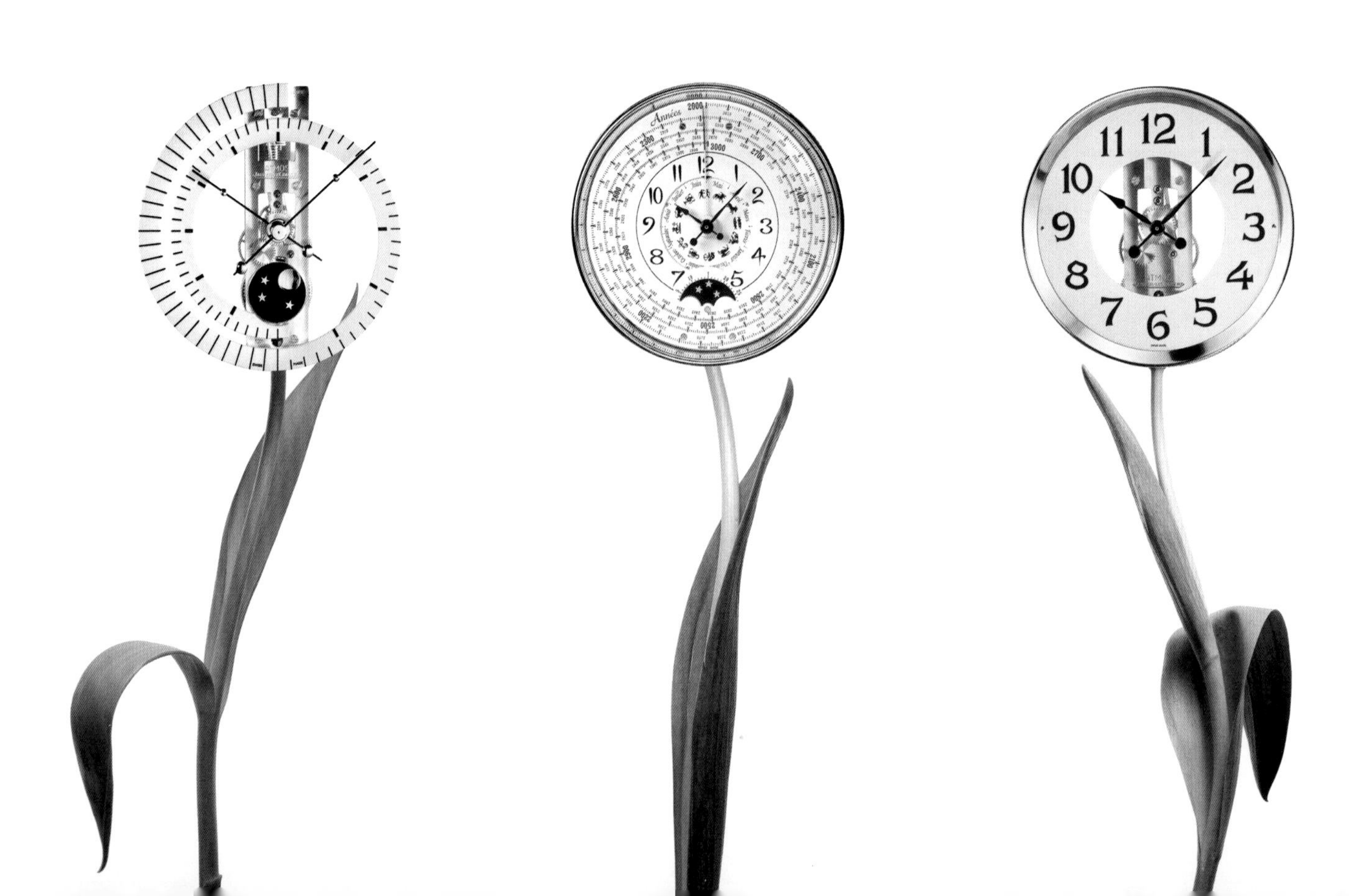
Années

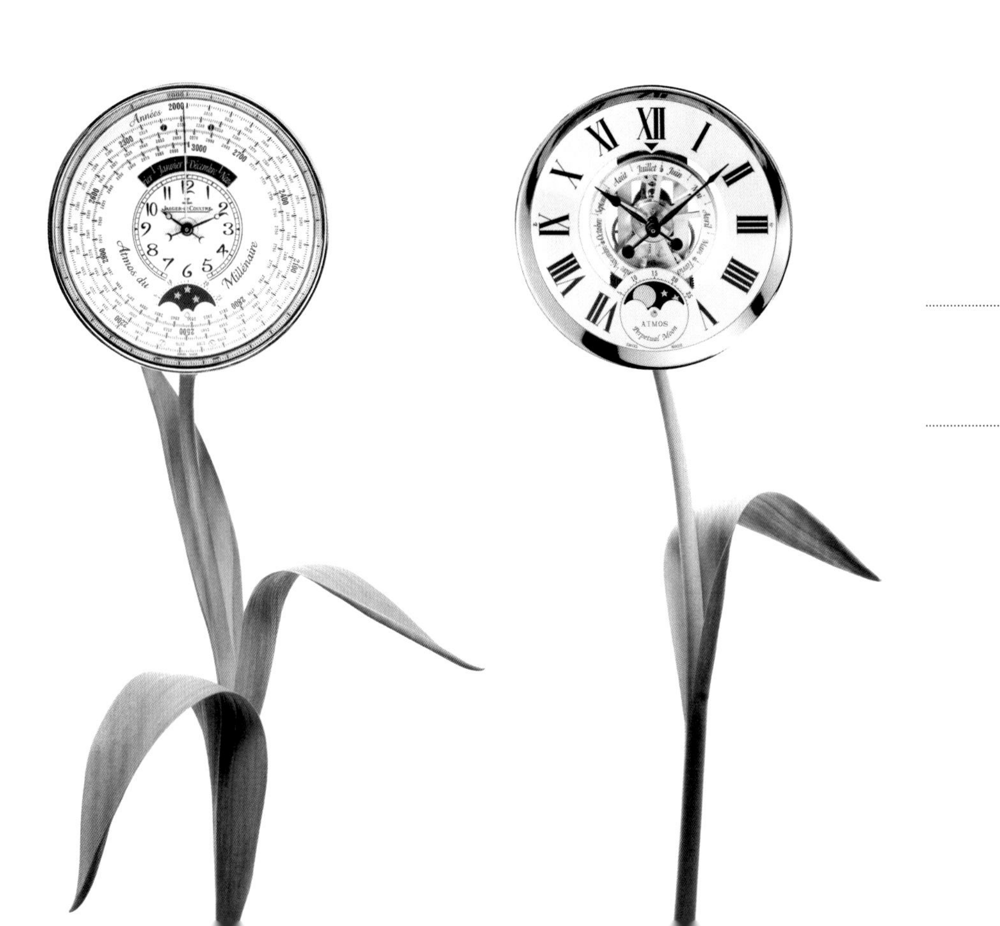

X

Atmos

The clock that lives on air

Atmos

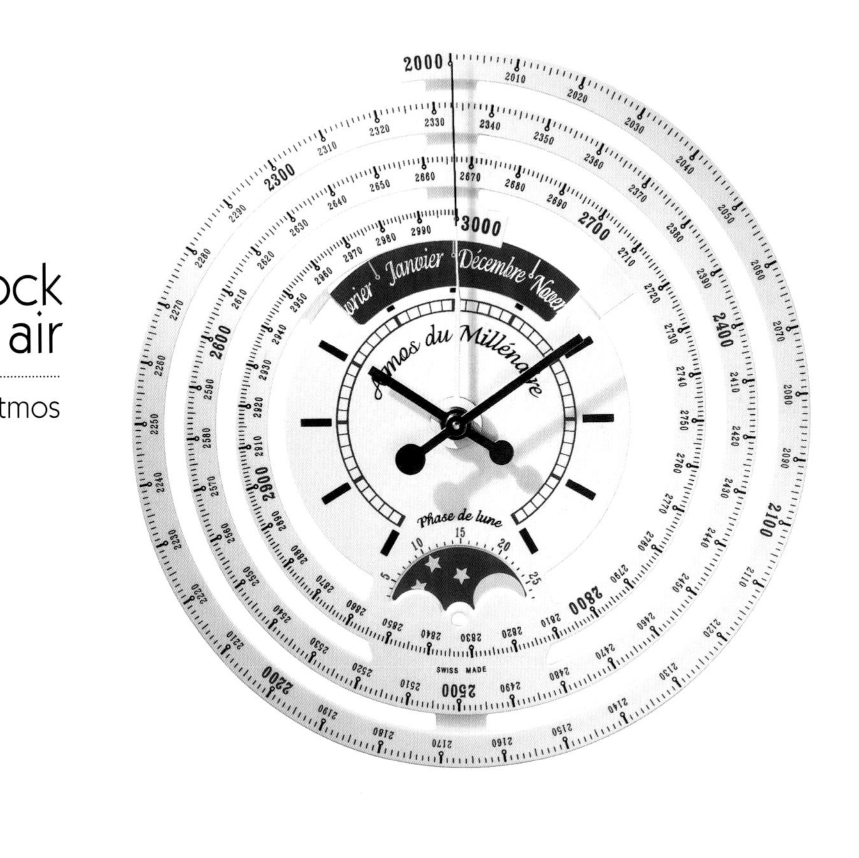

J.-L. Reutter, a young engineer from Neuchâtel, invented the working principle of the Atmos in 1928.

Atmos clock. First prototype made in 1928 by its inventor, J.-L. Reutter.

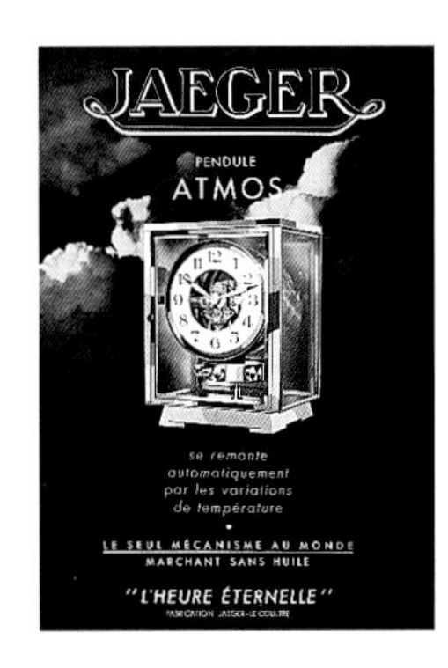

One of the earliest Atmos advertisements, first published by the Manufacture Jaeger-LeCoultre around 1930.

Leonardo da Vinci may have been able to demonstrate the physical impossibility of constructing a perpetual motion machine, but that has not stopped people from continually trying to do so.

In 1928, for example, a Neuchâtel engineer called Jean-Léon Reutter built a clock driven quite literally by air. It took the Jaeger-LeCoultre workshop a few more years to convert this idea into a technical form that could be patented, and to perfect it to such a degree that the Atmos practically achieved perpetual motion.

The technical principle is a beguiling one: a hermetically sealed capsule is filled with a gas which expands as the temperature rises and contracts as it falls, making the capsule move like a concertina. This motion constantly winds up the mainspring, a variation in temperature of only one degree in the range between 15 and 30 degrees centigrade being sufficient for two days' operation. To convert this small amount of energy into motion, everything inside the Atmos naturally has to work as smoothly and quietly as possible. The balance, for example, executes only two torsional semi-oscillations per minute, which is 60 times slower than the pendulum in a conventional clock. So it is not surprising that 60 million Atmos clocks together consume no more

Patented motor CH 175.399.

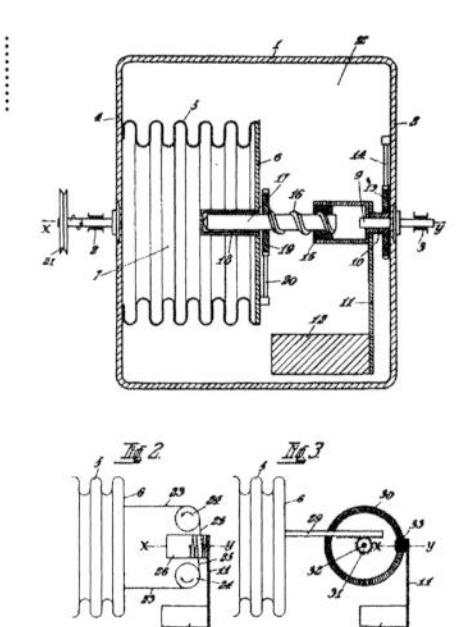

"Living on air." The history of the Atmos clock, written by Jean Lebet.

energy that one 15-watt light bulb. All its other parts, too, are of the highest precision. Admirers of advanced technology, however, are not the only ones who get their money's worth. Connoisseurs of elegant forms, precious materials and traditional craftmanship do so as well,because every Atmos is still made entirely by hand. With some models a single clock takes a whole month to produce, not counting the five weeks of trial and adjustment that every Atmos has to undergo. Only then are Jaeger-LeCoultre master-watchmakers satisfied enough to authenticate an Atmos clock with a signature and allow another one to leave the workshop. Subsequently, many end up in the very best of homes, because for decades the world's most celebrated watchmaking country has been presenting its distinguished guests with this masterpiece of Swiss artistry. The Atmos has had the honour of associating with great statesmen, royalty, and other renowned people including President John F. Kennedy, Sir Winston Churchill, General de Gaulle and Charlie Chaplin.

The Atmos clock is unique in the world. Its energy is drawn uniquely from variations in temperature. Its balance will oscillate for as long as the sun continues to shine.

When the temperature rises, a mixture of gas expands in the expansion chamber (1), which then compresses a spiral spring (3).

With a fall in temperature, the gas condenses and the spring slackens. This tiny back-and-forth motion is sufficient to wind up the Atmos.

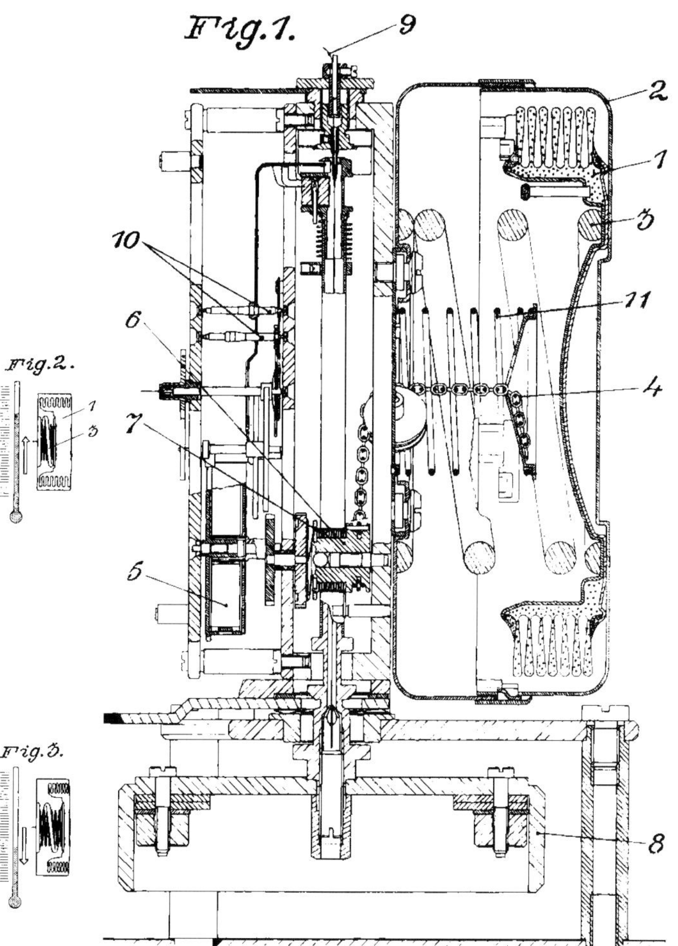

1. Expansion chamber
2. Cover
3. Motor spring (counterweight)
4. Chain
5. Mainspring
6. Pulley
7. Small spring
8. Balance wheel
9. Elinvar wire
10. Escapement
11. Winding spring

A monument
of unruffled
serenity

Atmos Classique

Simple architecture based on sleek, flowing lines, a virtually perpetual movement, in perfect harmony with nature. The Atmos Classique affirms a determination to achieve balance and modernity which reflects the genius of the famous clock: it infuses time with wonder and gently inhales the fragrance of eternity.

The Atmos has become the official gift of the Swiss Confederation. Some of the famous names who received one: John Fitzgerald Kennedy, Princess Irene of the Netherlands, King Hussein of Jordan, Richard Nixon,Sir Winston Churchill, Charles de Gaulle, Habib Bourguiba, Ronald Reagan, James McDivitt, Edgar White, Charlie Chaplin, Pope John Paul II.

While technology and so-called progress are constantly accelerating the pace of time and requiring ever greater amounts of energy, the Atmos lives accurately and silently on... air, with no need for batteries, electric current or rewinding.

Its balance swings gently, its "lung" breathing in perfect harmony with variations in temperature and its heart keeping up a steady two beats a minute, which is 60 times less than that of a conventional clock, 240 times less than a wristwatch movement, and 1,966,000 times less than a quartz watch. Through the simple, sparing lines of its architecture, the Atmos Classique asserts the sheer genius of its operational mode. In the same spirit of understatement, it enters the new millennium enhanced by a subtly innovative design. As if to affirm its determination to achieve balance and a resolutely modern

At its launch in the 1920s, Atmos heralded a revolutionary concept. Still unequalled today, it continues to glide through time on a breath of eternity.

The slightest variation in temperature infuses the Atmos with the energy needed to drive its movement.

approach, Jaeger-LeCoultre has created a pedestal with two feet, each resting on twin columns. The Atmos Classique with its almost perpetual movement stands proudly as a monument to unruffled serenity. The new cabinet housing the clock that lives on air comes in gold-plated and rhodium-plated versions, displaying the hours on a dial with Roman numerals or, for the very first time, Linton numerals. Naturally, this tribute to the atmosphere, living in tune with the rotation of the earth and the moon, never neglects one of its most specific tasks: to reflect the progress of the moon across the heavens. The Atmos Classique also features the month in its moon-phase version, an indication it displays with exceptional accuracy for around 4,000 years. The 24-carat gold-plated moon, as depicted on the Atmos against the backdrop of a starry night sky, displays the actual phases of the lunar month – known as the synodical revolution, meaning the time that elapses between two full moons. For the moon as a satellite of the earth to occupy the same position in relation to the sun, it must cover an additional distance on its orbit. This means that the lunar month lasts slightly longer than the sidereal revolution, i.e. an average of 29 days, 12 hours, 44 minutes and 2.8 seconds (29.530588 days).
The mechanism of your Atmos is so precise that it completes the revolution in 29.530568 days, involving a minimal difference per lunar month which will amount to only one day in 3,821 years.
A special implement supplied with your Atmos will enable your 130th descendant to return the moon to its correct phase in the year 5,823.

Atmos Classique.
24-carat gold-plated
and polished case.

510 12 02
W x D x H:
200 x 155 x 225 mm.

Atmos Classique.
Rhodium-plated
and polished case.

510 21 01
W x D x H:
200 x 155 x 225 mm.

Atmos Classique.
Moon phases and months.
24-carat gold-plated
and polished case.

511 12 02
W x D x H:
200 x 155 x 225 mm.

Atmos Classique.
Moon phases and months.
Rhodium-plated
and polished case.

511 22 02
W x D x H:
200 x 155 x 225 mm.

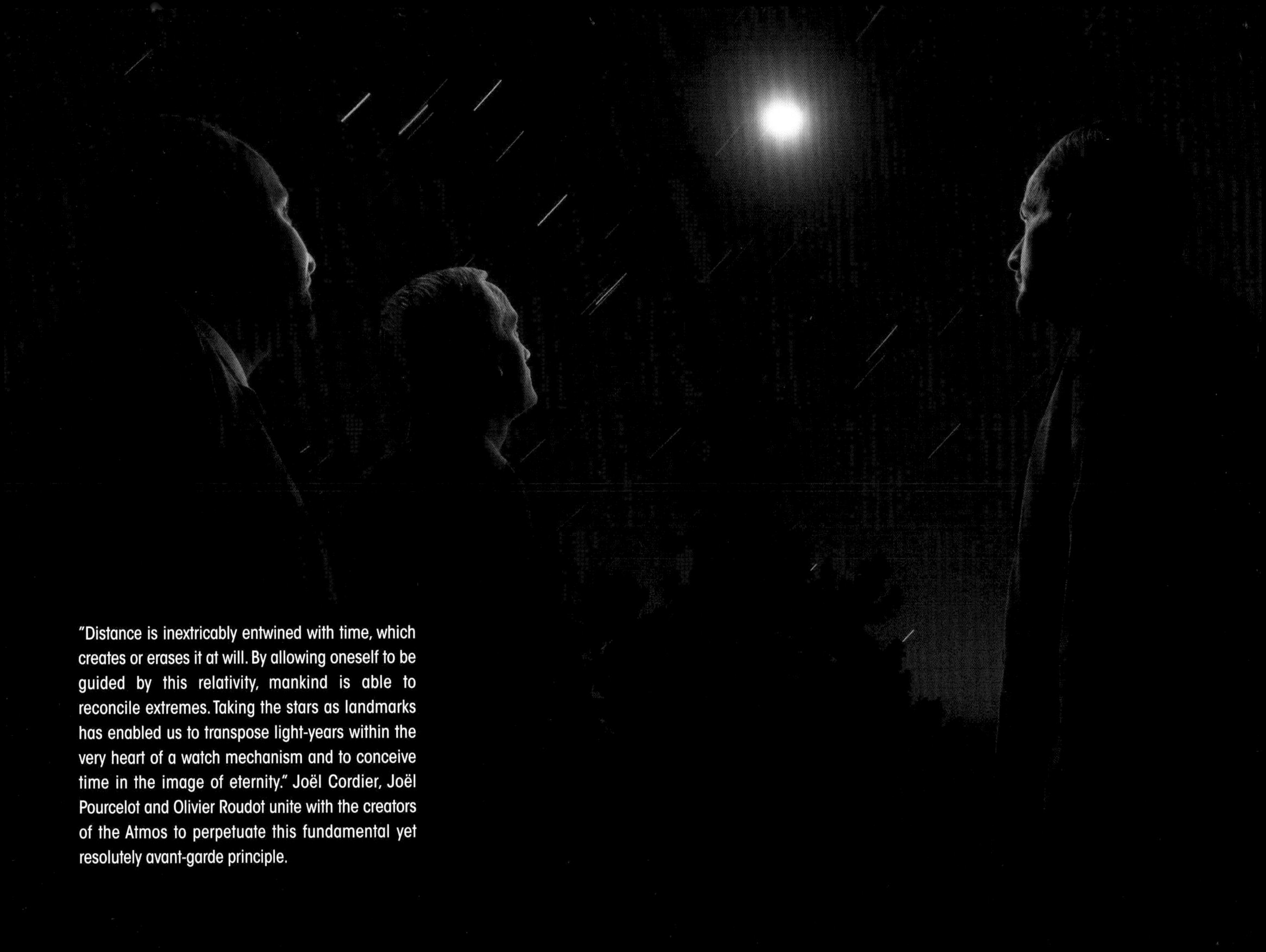

"Distance is inextricably entwined with time, which creates or erases it at will. By allowing oneself to be guided by this relativity, mankind is able to reconcile extremes. Taking the stars as landmarks has enabled us to transpose light-years within the very heart of a watch mechanism and to conceive time in the image of eternity." Joël Cordier, Joël Pourcelot and Olivier Roudot unite with the creators of the Atmos to perpetuate this fundamental yet resolutely avant-garde principle.

The Atmos
in its cosmic
version

Atmos 3000

The Atmos, which lives on air, is endowed with a fascinating set of gears which reflects the intricacies of celestial "mechanisms".

On its blue-lacquered disc with white transfers, the months measure off the passing of the years. In this way, the Atmos du Millénaire guides you steadily through the centuries, from generation to generation.

The Atmos du Millénaire goes beyond the traditional human scale of time measurement: to lead you towards the fourth millennium, the year display has been promoted to the position of main function.

In perfect harmony with nature, the Atmos du Millénaire will reflect the moon phases without the slightest "dark spot". You will be able to follow the movements of the night-time celestial body on its dedicated blue-lacquered disc with polished moon.

There is scarcely a step from the Atmos to the cosmos. That step was taken by the thrilling design which weds the famous clock by Jaeger-LeCoultre with the myth of space. Its virtually perpetual movement appears almost ready to launch out into the infinite.

French designer Robert Kohler was fascinated by the slow, silent oscillations of the Jaeger-LeCoultre Atmos clock, which draws its energy from the air around it. Suspended in its crystal-clear glass capsule evoking its intimate dependency on air, the Atmos 3000 appears to be floating in space, like a star beyond the realms of gravity. The three cones supporting its pedestal resemble rockets ready to thrust its virtually perpetual movement into the realms of heavenly mechanisms. And, on the endless spiral of its grooved dial, the fractions of time which follow each other, peacefully and tirelessly, appear to catch and hold a glimpse of eternity for those who spend but a fleeting moment here on earth. As if to signify that the minutes, hours and months merely serve to reflect the tiny human scale of things, the Atmos du Millénaire offers a year display as its main function. Driven by rhodium-plated Calibre 556 with its ultra-thin stud balance, it will prove capable of managing its time for a thousand years, smoothly unveiling the moon phases as it proceeds. And if your encounter with

The moon rises and sets infallibly for nearly 4,000 years.

this Atmos makes you feel that the millennial scale is too overwhelming, the centre hour and minute hands will always help to thrust you right back into the down-to-earth realities of daily life. Its highly futurist design expresses all the spirit and charm of post-modernism. The mineral glass case rests on a trapeze-shaped base, mounted on three metallic cones. Its spiral white-lacquered brass dial with transferred numerals is enhanced by a blue-lacquered month disc with white transfers. The extremely slow forward motion of the year hand on the Atmos du Millénaire will provide a touch of serenity amid the headlong rush of time, and will do so for a very, very long time... While the Atmos has already built its own legend, this special contribution by the Manufacture to the arrival of the new millennium soars skywards in inimitable fashion, undeniably bound for eternity.

Flat balance with 12 motifs, oscillating 30 seconds in one direction, 30 seconds in the other, meaning 120 vibrations/hour.

Atmos du Millénaire.
Years, months
and moon phases.
Rhodium-plated
and polished feet.

532 23 01
W x D x H:
250 x 152 x 275 mm.

Atmos 3000.
Moon phases.
Rhodium-plated
and polished feet.

531 23 01
W x D x H:
250 x 152 x 275 mm.

Atmos Marqueterie

Capable of running smoothly through a millennium, it combines the signs of the zodiac with the moon-phase display on its dial. And to protect this technological marvel, the cabinet is an inimitably rare object that revives the art of marquetry-work at its most refined.

An intimate personal messenger, the Atmos du Millénaire Marqueterie houses ten tubes in its secret drawer: each contains a parchment on which to write your stories and hand them down to your descendants, who will in turn commit their own experiences to the same confidant.

The receptacle of a thousand years of memories, the Atmos du Millénaire Marqueterie provides everything to ensure that your meaningful moments and those of coming generations are inscribed in eternity, including a solidified stick of India ink with a stone inkwell and a gold-plated penholder.

The eleventh tube in the drawer contains the tool for setting the months, years and moon phases. No other mechanical clock in the world provides such ideal conditions for a one-thousand year journey.

The Atmos Marqueterie is an artistic and timekeeping witness to a wealth of patiently cultivated expertise. In its Millénaire version, it brings the previous millennium to a triumphant conclusion and becomes the receptacle for the transition from one generation to the next.

In our high-tech age, wood has been chosen to honour the timeless nature of the Atmos, unmatched since 1928. For the rare circle of master cabinetmakers, this object has provided them with a chance to give free rein to their passion. The Atmos Marqueterie, representing a genuine rebirth of rare and precious wood, has an inimitable character which gives it an exclusive allure that is fully appreciated by genuine connoisseurs of fine watchmaking. Restraint plays no role here; passion and immoderation alone could inspire such an incredibly complex creation. Only the talent of Jérôme Boutteçon, a marquetry-work specialist based in the Swiss Jura who won the title of Best Craftsman in France in 1994, could accomplish this lengthy, meticulous task. Wood, life, the perpetual renaissance of art through time... Marquetry-work is also the finest reflection of the transition between successive generations. Jaeger-LeCoultre has therefore made it a witness to the most intimate personal values, by creating the Atmos du Millénaire in its Marqueterie and Marqueterie Astrale versions. Because everyone would wish to leave a trace of their experience here on earth, this exceptional masterpiece will be a worthy receptacle of one thousand years of life's highlights, traditions,

feelings and joys, which will inevitably flow with the current of passing generations. In its secret drawer, ten lacquered and engraved tubes are ready to welcome the stories and secrets of each individual during the next ten centuries. There is one tube per century, each containing a sheet of parchment. Moreover, a leather pouch holds a stick of solidified India ink and a stone inkwell. The secret drawer also reveals a penholder, ensuring that the great family accomplishments or the key events of the millennium may be written down and preserved for posterity. Love stories, important dates, extraordinary and moving memories: all will give personal shape to the history of time. The Atmos du Millénaire Marqueterie is designed in keeping with the original Atmos clock. Powered by air, it houses Calibre 555, which greets eternity with amazing faithfulness, gently beating to the rhythm of minutes, hours, months, years and moon phases. This clock is also a supremely refined piece

In its odyssey down through the centuries, the Atmos du Millénaire Marqueterie is accompanied by a superb natural leather travel trunk which alone weighs 50 kg. Its 16 drawers in exotic woods will enable you to fondly conceal treasured heirlooms.

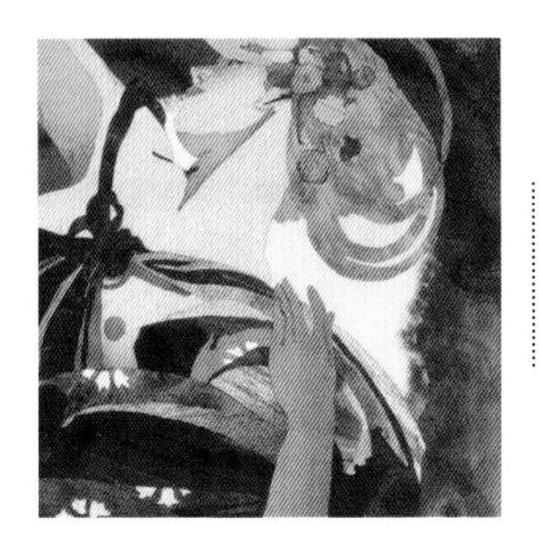

Around forty types of wood and more than 500 delicately crafted parts were required to create the works of art evocatively entitled "Clair de Lune" and "Etoile du Soir", gentle messengers from the star-lit sky.

of furniture. Its cabinet is made up of several dozen different types of wood, delicately fashioned to create a faithful reproduction of the works of Alfons Mucha, such as "Aurore" and "Crépuscule", remarkable witnesses to Art Nouveau. For the Atmos du Millénaire Marqueterie version, the softly shivering feminine forms of "Aurore" and "Crépuscule" illustrate humankind's hesitations when faced with the unknown at the turn of the century. Meanwhile, the Atmos du Millénaire Marqueterie Astrale embraces the celestial luminosity of the "Etoile du Matin", "Clair de Lune" and "Etoile du Soir", a theme that is given an almost visionary spirit by the signs of the zodiac gracing the dial. Jérôme Boutteçon, an amazingly talented marquetry craftsman, hones each of his works to perfection with meticulous care, meaning that only a few such creations may be completed each month. This implies that each Atmos du Millénaire Marqueterie clock can justifiably claim to be unique.

Designed to accompany successive generations over a thousand-year period, the Atmos du Millénaire Marqueterie conveys a sense of eternity through its dial. It faithfully marks off the time in a marvellously accurate manner, beating to the rhythm of minutes, hours, months, years and moon phases.

Atmos du Millénaire
Marqueterie Astrale.
Rare wood.
Years, months, moon phases
and signs of the zodiac.

553 31 01
W x D x H:
310 x 242 x 365 mm.

Atmos du Millénaire Marqueterie.
Rare wood.
Years, months,
moon phases.

552 31 01
W x D x H:
310 x 242 x 365 mm.

"Swept along by his passion, the artisan of time becomes a reflection of the perpetual renewal of nature. Our thirst for truth, for improvement and creative freedom constantly drives us beyond existing limits. Representing the fruit of science and art, midway between technology and emotion, each timekeeper becomes a new universal point of reference." Led by master-watchmaker Eric Coudray and all the pioneers of the Manufacture, this journey to the heart of the watch opens up boundless unexplored horizons…

Creation:
Grey Worldwide S.A., Geneva

Photography:
Peter Hebeisen, Paris
Nick Welsh, Geneva
Lionel Flusin, Viry
Photo 2000, La Chaux-de-Fonds
Dieter Blum, Esslingen

Lithography:
Zuliani S.A., Montreux

Printing:
Courvoisier-Attinger S.A., Bienne

Printed in Switzerland.

2002/2003 Edition. Models and technical specifications may be subject to change.

Jaeger-LeCoultre S.A., rue de la Golisse 8, CH-1347 Le Sentier
www.mjlc.com